CHICAGO WILDERNESS

A Regional Nature Reserve

An Atlas of Biodiversity

CHICAGO WILDERNESS

A Regional Nature Reserve

Chicago Wilderness, An Atlas of Biodiversity,
is a publication of the Chicago Region Biodiversity Council.
The members of the Council include:

Brookfield Zoo
Canal Corridor Association
Chicago Academy of Sciences
Chicago Botanic Garden
Chicago Park District
City of Chicago, Department of Environment
The Field Museum
Forest Preserve District of Cook County
Forest Preserve District of DuPage County
Forest Preserve District of Will County
Friends of the Chicago River
Illinois Department of Natural Resources
Illinois Natural History Survey
Illinois Nature Preserves Commission
Kane County Forest Preserve District
Lake County Forest Preserves
Lake Michigan Federation
Lincoln Park Zoo
McHenry County Conservation District
Metropolitan Water Reclamation District of Greater Chicago
Morton Arboretum
The Nature Conservancy
Northeastern Illinois Planning Commission
Openlands Project
John G. Shedd Aquarium
Sierra Club, Illinois Chapter
Urban Resources Partnership
US Army Corps of Engineers, Chicago District
US Environmental Protection Agency, Region V
US EPA Great Lakes National Program Office
USDA Forest Service
USDA Natural Resources Conservation Service
USDI Fish & Wildlife Service
USDI National Park Service

Funds for this publication were provided by:
Illinois Conservation Foundation
The Nature Conservancy of Illinois
State of Illinois Department of Natural Resources, Conservation 2000 Fund
US EPA Great Lakes National Program Office
USDA Forest Service Northeastern Area, State and Private Forestry
USDI Fish & Wildlife Service, Chicago, Illinois Field Office

Written by Jerry Sullivan
Designed by Corasue Nicholas
Printed in Mexico

CONTENTS

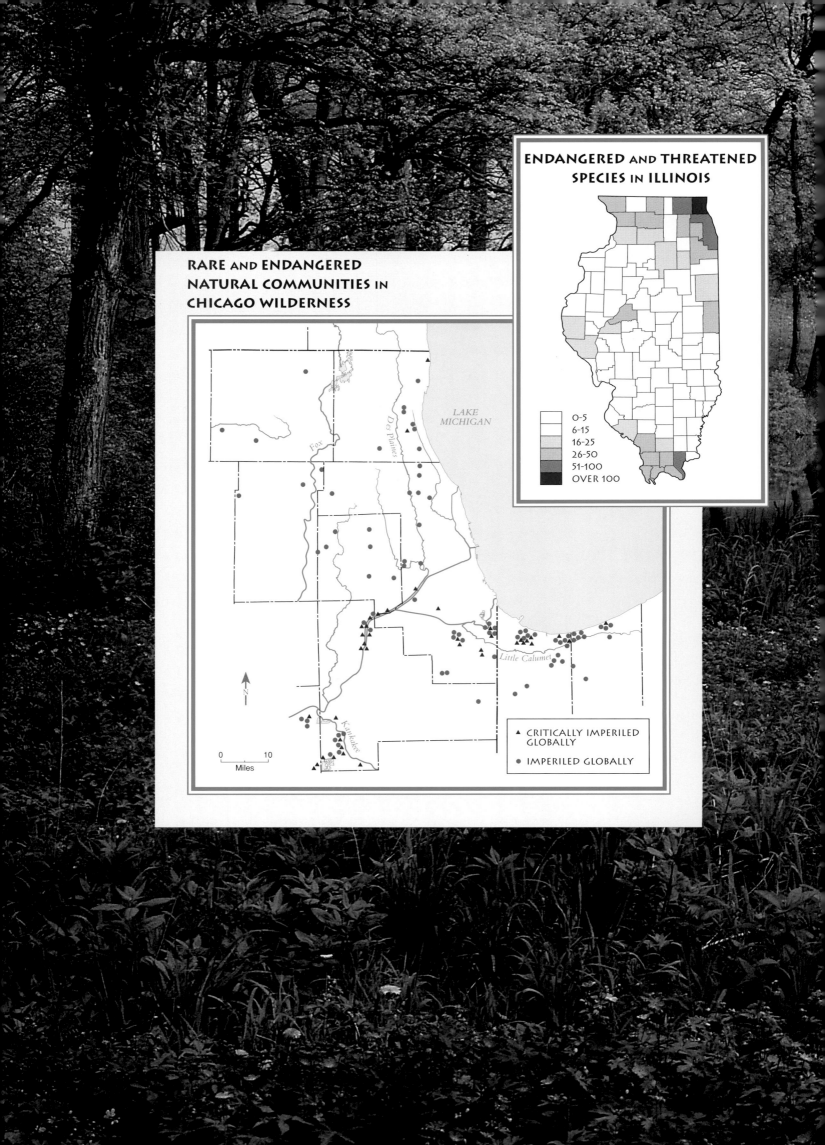

ENDANGERED AND THREATENED SPECIES IN ILLINOIS

0-5
6-15
16-25
26-50
51-100
OVER 100

RARE AND ENDANGERED NATURAL COMMUNITIES IN CHICAGO WILDERNESS

LAKE MICHIGAN

Fox

Des Plaines

Little Calumet

Kankakee

N

0   10
Miles

▲ CRITICALLY IMPERILED GLOBALLY

● IMPERILED GLOBALLY

NATURE IN THE METROPOLIS

The Story of Chicago Wilderness

The lands stretching south and west from the shores of Lake Michigan hold one of North America's great metropolises. Nearly eight million people live in northwestern Indiana, northeastern Illinois, and southeastern Wisconsin. Living among them, on islands of green, are thousands of native species of plants and animals, species that make up some of the rarest natural communities on earth. We call these communities and the lands and waters that are their homes Chicago Wilderness. Communities like these—prairies, oak savannas, woodlands, marshes, fens, sedge meadows and others—once covered most of the Midwest. They have been destroyed almost everywhere to make way for towns and farms.

Only small fragments survive, and many of the richest of these fragments are in Chicago Wilderness. The largest metropolis in the region is also home to the finest surviving examples of the natural heritage of the Midwest.

More than one-third of Illlinois' dedicated nature preserves are in the six counties of Chicago Wilderness.

The maps on the facing page suggest what is at stake. They show the concentration of rare animals and plants and the dense clusters of whole natural communities that may vanish from the face of the earth if they are not protected in Chicago Wilderness.

This Atlas provides an introduction to these endangered communities. It tells how they sustain themselves and how natural forces—and people—have shaped them over thousands of years. It describes efforts to use land preservation and ecological restoration to save them and tells where interested people can see them.

A combination of enlightened action and historical accident has thus far prevented the extinction of the natural wonders of Chicago Wilderness. They will survive into the next century only if we act to ensure that survival.

GEOLOGY OF THE CHICAGO WILDERNESS REGION

Ice built the landscape of the Chicago Wilderness. Major construction began about 26,000 years ago and ended about 13,000 years ago when the glaciers receded from the Chicago region for the last time. Even after the ice had gone, the after effects of glaciation repeatedly remade the shoreline of Lake Michigan. The lake stabilized at its present size just 2,000 years ago.

The Ice Age, geologists call it the Pleistocene, saw four major ice advances in eastern North America. The first occurred about 500,000 years ago. The last—the Wisconsin stage—began about 70,000 years ago. At one time, the Wisconsin ice spread as far as Shelbyville, Illinois, 200 miles south of Chicago. Our landscape reveals the complex series of ice movements that occurred during the later years of the Wisconsin glacial episode.

The glaciers that covered our region were as much as a quarter of a mile thick. Land around the northern Great Lakes is still rising, still rebounding from the weight placed upon it by the ice thousands of years ago.

It would seem that something that big could go wherever it wanted to go, but in fact, the land under the ice exerted a powerful influence on glacial movements. In central North America, the ice followed river valleys, and over the course of the Pleistocene, scoured those valleys into the deep, broad basins that now hold the Great Lakes. The landscape of the Chicago region records five major advances of the ice out of the Lake Michigan basin alternating with periods when the ice retreated to the basin.

The glacial constructions cover a bedrock foundation made of very old sedimentary rocks.   In the Chicago region, the most common type of bedrock is a magnesium-rich limestone called dolomite that was originally deposited on reefs set in shallow seas during the Silurian period about 400 million years ago. The youngest bedrock in our region dates from the Pennsylvanian period about 300 million years ago. This is the rock that contains the coal deposits in Will County.

There are highlands and valleys in our bedrock, but none of them corresponds to the highlands and valleys visible at the surface. The surface features are all made of material deposited by the glaciers or by the lakes that appeared as the glaciers melted. In some places, these deposits are nearly 400 feet thick. Only along the Des Plaines River in southwestern Cook and western Will Counties are bedrock exposures large enough to have an effect on living things. There, unique communities of plants and animals live on soils only a few inches thick that lie above the Silurian dolomite bedrock.

GLACIAL DRIFT

Drift is the traditional term for the material left behind by glaciers. There are two kinds of drift. *Till* is material that was deposited directly from the glacier. *Outwash* is material deposited by meltwater flowing from the glacier.

Glaciers are supreme earth movers. As their enormous weight scrapes across the ground, they easily collect loose surface deposits. Bedrock is harder to dislodge, but they manage to collect it as well. Frozen into the ice as a totally unsorted mixture of giant boulders, cobbles, gravel, sand, silt, and the finest of clay particles, drift can be carried hundreds of miles. When glaciers begin to melt, this material drops out and piles up in front of the ice. Glaciers are always moving, and sometimes their rate of movement is equal to their rate of

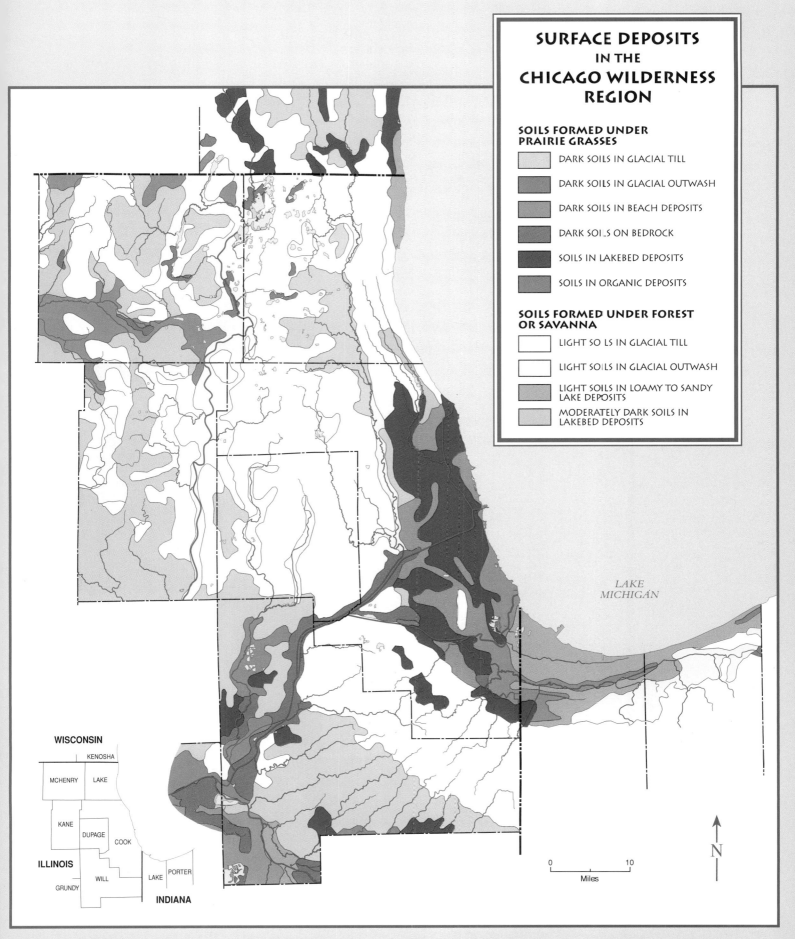

SURFACE DEPOSITS IN THE CHICAGO WILDERNESS REGION

SOILS FORMED UNDER PRAIRIE GRASSES

- DARK SOILS IN GLACIAL TILL
- DARK SOILS IN GLACIAL OUTWASH
- DARK SOILS IN BEACH DEPOSITS
- DARK SOILS ON BEDROCK
- SOILS IN LAKEBED DEPOSITS
- SOILS IN ORGANIC DEPOSITS

SOILS FORMED UNDER FOREST OR SAVANNA

- LIGHT SOILS IN GLACIAL TILL
- LIGHT SOILS IN GLACIAL OUTWASH
- LIGHT SOILS IN LOAMY TO SANDY LAKE DEPOSITS
- MODERATELY DARK SOILS IN LAKEBED DEPOSITS

LAKE MICHIGAN

WISCONSIN

KENOSHA

MCHENRY | LAKE

KANE

DUPAGE | COOK

ILLINOIS

GRUNDY | WILL | LAKE | PORTER

INDIANA

0 — 10
Miles

N

Deposits left by the glaciers or by the lakes that formed as the glaciers melted are the raw materials of soils. Topography, drainage, climate, and vegetation shape these raw materials into soils. The process takes centuries. In a dynamic landscape, vegetation may change more rapidly than soils. We may find prairies growing on forest soils and forests on prairie soils. The scale of the map allows us to show only broad categories. Small patches of soil that do not match the surrounding land will not appear.

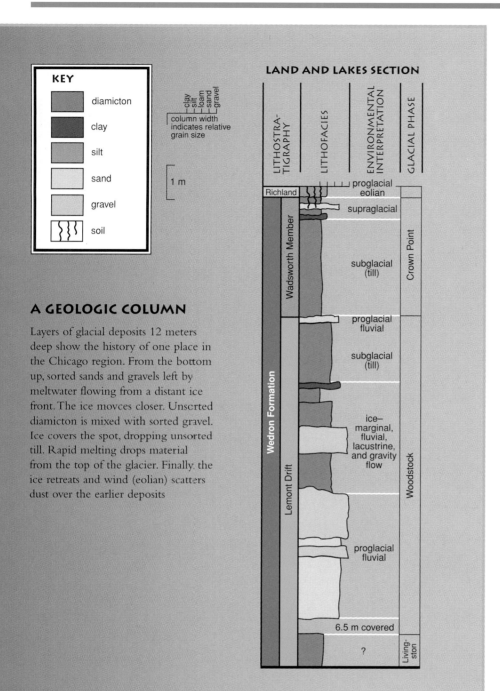

KEY

	diamicton
	clay
	silt
	sand
	gravel
	soil

column width indicates relative grain size

clay silt loam sand gravel

1 m

LAND AND LAKES SECTION

LITHOSTRA- TIGRAPHY | LITHOFACIES | ENVIRONMENTAL INTERPRETATION | GLACIAL PHASE

Richland — proglacial eolian

Wadsworth Member — supraglacial — Crown Point

subglacial (till)

proglacial fluvial

subglacial (till)

Lemont Drift — ice— marginal, fluvial, lacustrine, and gravity flow — Woodstock

Wedron Formation

proglacial fluvial

6.5 m covered

? — Livingston

A GEOLOGIC COLUMN

Layers of glacial deposits 12 meters deep show the history of one place in the Chicago region. From the bottom up, sorted sands and gravels left by meltwater flowing from a distant ice front. The ice movces closer. Unscrted diamicton is mixed with sorted gravel. Ice covers the spot, dropping unsorted till. Rapid melting drops material from the top of the glacier. Finally, the ice retreats and wind (eolian) scatters dust over the earlier deposits

melting. Geologists call such times "still stands." The ice front appears to be standing still, but it is really acting like a giant conveyor carrying an endless supply of fresh drift to the ice front.

At a stationary ice front, heaps of drift can form hills hundreds of feet high. Since these hills are made of till, they are an unsorted mixture of everything from rocks the size of garages to microscopic clay particles. Immense blocks of ice break off from the melting glacier and are buried in this debris. As they melt, they form ponds and lakes.

The landscapes created by these conditions are called *moraines*. Moraines are places where

knobby hills and ridges are mixed with kettle-holes where blocks of ice melted into lakes and marshes. The Chicago region has hundreds of square miles of moraines where the varied landscape supports a rich assortment of natural communities that are home to much of the biodiversity of the Chicago wilderness.

When a glacier a quarter of a mile thick begins to melt, it floods the land with cascades, torrents, whole lakes full of water. In our region, many proglacial lakes were dammed between the ice front and older moraines. They filled, endured for a few decades or a few centuries, and drained away. Rivers a mile wide scoured valleys. In some places the water just poured over the land in sheets.

Water sorts the particles it carries. It takes a heavy, powerful flow to push a boulder along. As the current slows, smaller and smaller particles settle to the bottom: gravel, sand, and silt along rivers; clays in the lake bottoms. Much of the surface deposits on the lowlands lying between the moraines in the Chicago Wilderness are made of outwash.

SHAPING THE LAND

The ice advance of 26,000 years ago that began the process of shaping our landscape brought the ice front to the Marengo Moraine, often called the Marengo Ridge, which runs north and south through western McHenry County to Kane County. This is the westernmost and oldest of the moraines in our region.

The push south to Shelbyville came after the building of the Marengo Ridge, but by about 17,500 years ago, the ice front had once again melted back to the Chicago area. This was the beginning of a very eventful few thousand years. The ice, in a complex dance of advance-retreat-readvance built a zone of overlapping moraines that extends from western Kane County to the shore of Lake Michigan. The ice moved rapidly—by glacial standards—and each episode of moraine building was followed by a retreat when the ice melted back—often as far as the Lake Michigan Basin.

The oldest moraines in our region are to the west and south. The land gets progressively younger toward Lake Michigan. Our largest moraine belt is the Valparaiso Moraine which runs south through Lake, Cook, and DuPage Counties before swinging east through Will County and Lake and Porter Counties in

GLACIAL PROCESSES

A glacier melts back from an end moraine. The moraine acts as a dam, holding in the waters of a proglacial lake. The water cuts a single outlet channel through the moraine. As the lake drains away, the lake bottom becomes a plain marked with sandy beach ridges located along the old shoreline.

Meltwater swirls down through a hole in the ice. The moving water carries away smaller particles, leaving a mound of gravel called a *kame*.

Meltwater flows under the ice in a winding channel like the meandering course of a river. With the ice gone, deposits left by the water make an *esker*, a ridge that winds like a river.

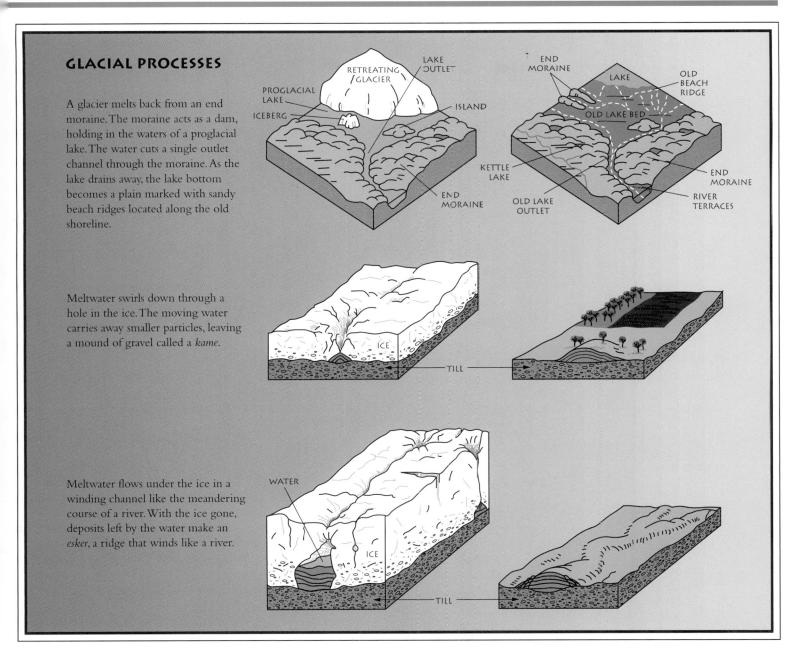

The narrow ridge of the Visitation Esker in southwestern Cook County meanders through Cap Sauer's Holdings, a Cook County Forest Preserve.

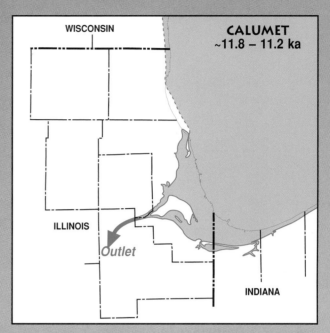

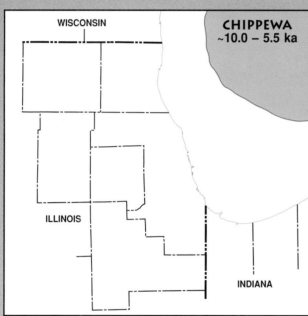

LAKE MICHIGAN'S EVENTFUL HISTORY

The lake began as a pro-glacial lake dammed between the ice front and the moraines that circle the southern end of the Lake Michigan Basin. This Glenwood Stage was 55 feet above the present level of the lake. Sand ridges on the moraines mark that early shore. The lake over-topped the moraine in what is now southwestern Cook County and rapidly eroded an outlet (the Sag Valley) nearly a mile wide.

The Calumet Stage was about 35 feet above the present level. Blue Island, where resistant bedrock had prevented erosion by the ice, stood above the water.

The low-water Chippewa Stage occurred when a temporary outlet opened for Lakes Michigan and Huron through North Bay, Ontario.

Water fell to 300 feet below the present level. Forests grew in what is now deep water.

Geologists call these early stages Lake Chicago. The title "Lake Michigan" refers to stages that occurred after ice had completely left the basin.

The Nipissing Phase of Lake Michigan saw water rising again over the lake plain and drainage from the lake flowing south through the Sag and down the Des Plaines to the Illinois. This phase left several prominent landmarks, including the beach ridge that provided the route for Clark Street in Chicago.

Indiana. The Valparaiso Moraine is as much as 25 miles wide with many high ridges and kettlehole lakes and marshes. Our youngest moraines are the Lake Border Moraines in Lake and northern Cook County, Illinois. Five separate Lake Border moraines, all lying parallel to the shore of Lake Michigan, have been named. The low areas between these moraines are the valleys of the Des Plaines and Chicago Rivers. Glaciers never returned to land in the Chicago region after the easternmost of these morainal ridges fell from the ice about 14,000 years ago.

However, the history of Lake Michigan was just beginning. The earliest proglacial lake, the Glenwood Phase of Lake Chicago, was 55 feet above the present mean level of Lake Michigan. As the lake went up and down with the geological changes that followed the retreat of the ice, it left behind beaches, sandspits, and thick layers of clay fallen from quiet waters. These features mark the largest of our lake plains, the Chicago Lake Plain. Most of the modern city is located on this plain.

The early stages of Lake Chicago drained south to the Illinois and Mississippi Rivers through a gap in the moraines called the Chicago Outlet in what is now southwestern Cook County. The rush of water through this gap cut the Sag Valley and eroded the Des Plaines River channel down to bedrock in Cook and Will Counties.

After cutting the channel of the Des Plaines down to bedrock, the lake stabilized for a time, then dropped again after a new outlet opened to the north, shutting down the so called Chicago outlet. However, the lake returned to the Chicago Outlet in later times, most recently during the Nipissing Phase of Lake Michigan, a period that ended only 4,000 years ago. The youngest land in the region is along the shore of Lake Michigan in northern Lake County (IL). The land in Illinois Beach State Park is sand deposited by lake currents since the end of the Nipissing Phase.

Since the ice departed, the pace and scope of change has drastically slowed. Deposits of wind blown dust called loess (pronounced "luss.") have accumulated on the glacial drift. Our rivers have cut more definite channels in the intermoraine areas, although marshes, bogs and other wetlands show that much of the land is poorly drained or not drained at all. Peat has built up in undrained basins and blowing sands have built the high dunes of the Indiana shore.

SOILS

The deposits left by the glaciers and the lake stages are the raw materials of soils. The soils themselves develop over centuries, products of climate, topography, and the effects of living things.

Soils that develop on hilltops are quite different from those that develop in low valleys—especially if the valleys are subject to regular flooding. Soils on steep slopes may erode as fast as they develop.

Soils developed under forests are quite distinct from those that were created under prairies. Wetland soils are equally distinctive. We will describe these soils in more detail in the coming pages.

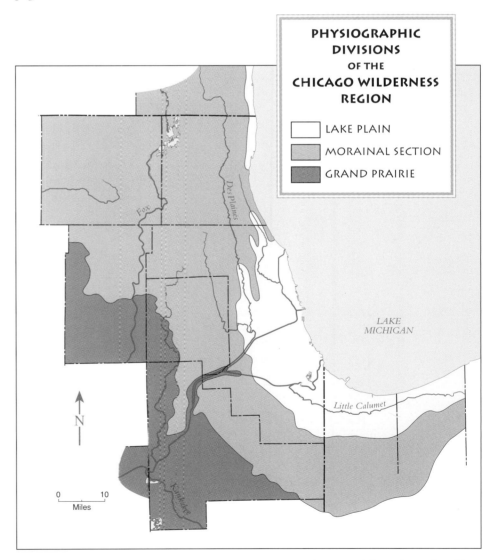

Chicago Wilderness is part of three separate physiographic regions. The regions differ in their geological history, their terrain, and their vegetation

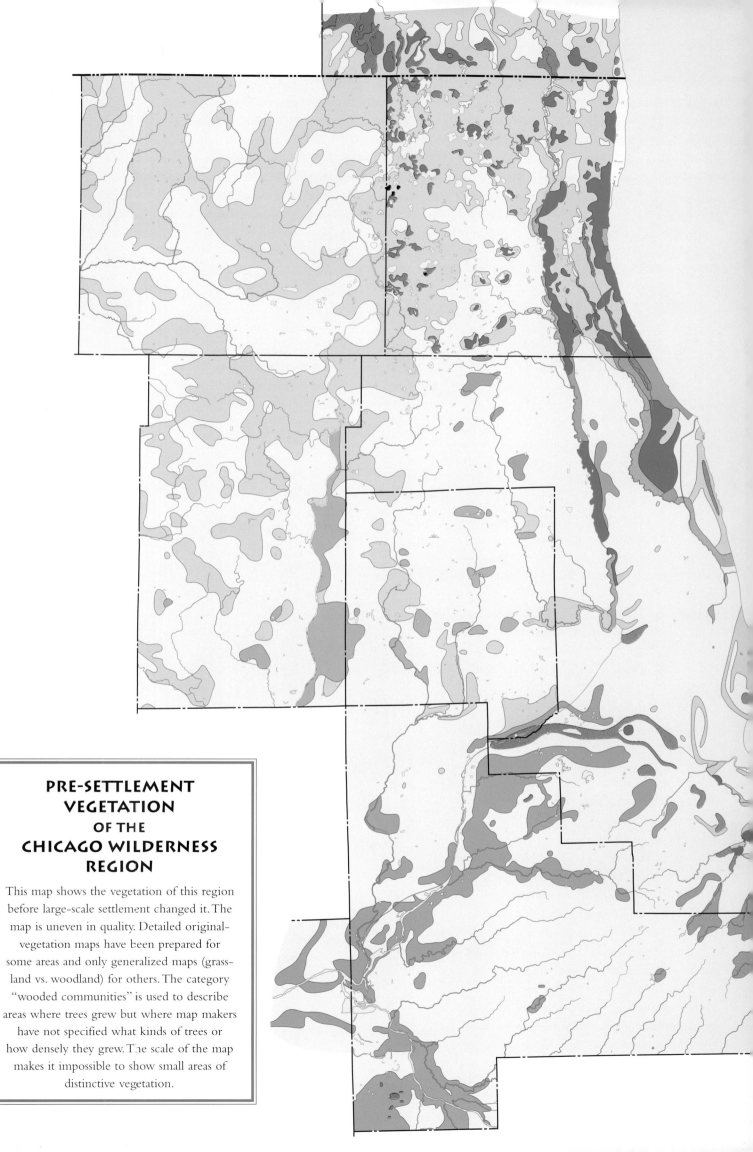

PRE-SETTLEMENT
VEGETATION
OF THE
CHICAGO WILDERNESS
REGION

This map shows the vegetation of this region
before large-scale settlement changed it. The
map is uneven in quality. Detailed original-
vegetation maps have been prepared for
some areas and only generalized maps (grassland vs. woodland) for others. The category
"wooded communities" is used to describe
areas where trees grew but where map makers
have not specified what kinds of trees or
how densely they grew. The scale of the map
makes it impossible to show small areas of
distinctive vegetation.

PRAIRIE

SAVANNA

WOODED COMMUNITIES

OAK WOODLAND

UPLAND FOREST

FLOODPLAIN FOREST

DUNE COMPLEX

WETLANDS

SWAMP

BOG

LAKES

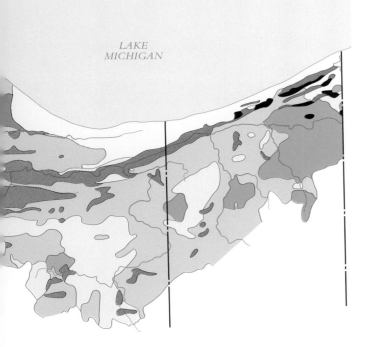

LAKE MICHIGAN

0   5   10
Miles

N

LIVING COMMUNITIES

*T*he varied landscape that remained when the ice departed and the lake retreated to its present shoreline is the base that supports the biodiversity of the Chicago Wilderness. Sands and clays, hilltops and plains offer different opportunities to different plants and animals. Geology, topography, and climate combine with living things to create *ecosystems*. When we talk of a prairie ecosystem or a forest ecosystem we include both the living things and the non-living things that have an effect on life.

The term *community* or *natural community* refers just to the living things in the ecosystem. Since plants respond more specifically to moisture and light, communities are usually described or named by the vegetation. The members of a natural community are connected in many ways, and these connections are so complicated that we will never understand all of them.

We do know that the loss of a single species in a community can lead to the loss of more species. A flower disappears because the insect that pollinated it is gone. Insects vanish because their food plants have died out.

Healthy natural communities have room for all their species. In healthy communities, we see biodiversity. "Biodiversity" refers to the variety of life, from variations in the genes of individuals to the whole planet and all its millions of species. On a regional level, biodiversity can refer to the many communities that exist side by side.

Biodiversity helps natural communities survive catastrophes. Indeed for some species, events such as floods and storms are opportunities rather than catastrophes.

In the Chicago Wilderness, we see biodiversity within communities and in the great variety of communities found in the region. We have nearly a dozen wooded communities. Our prairies are wet prairies, dry prairies, gravel hill prairies, and others. Our wetlands are a very diverse collection of marshes, fens, sedge meadows, bogs, and swamps. Each of these separate types has its own special combination of animals and plants.

The next section of this Atlas will introduce you to the natural communities of the Chicago Wilderness and describe some of the animals and plants that make their homes in these communities.

PRAIRIES

n all my life, I never saw or dreamed of so beautiful a sight as the rolling prairies. Nothing can equal the surpassing beauty of the rounded swells and the sunny hollows, the brilliant green of the grass, the numberless varieties and splendid hues of multitudes of flowers. I gazed in admiration too strong for words.

Ellen Bigelow
1835

Miss Bigelow's reaction was shared by many who were lucky enough to see the tallgrass prairie in all its glory. She was a New Englander who had grown up among forests. There are prairies as far east as Massachusetts, but they are small, sunny islands in a sea of trees. In the Illinois country, people moving west found tall waving grasses and the "splendid hues" of wildflowers covering much of the land. Here the prairies were the sea, and the woodlands were shady islands. The prairies of Illinois were the first real American experience of the wide-open spaces. Here you could find yourself in a prairie that stretched to the horizon, without a single tree in sight.

Many early visitors expected the prairies to be of little use to farmers. Their belief was that any soil too poor to grow trees was too poor to grow crops. Others noted the advantages of land that did not need to be cleared of trees. The prairie was instant pasture for cattle and horses and needed only a plow to make it ready to grow crops.

However, the first settlers who tried turning prairie sod with the light wooden plows they had used in the forests got a rather nasty shock. A plow that would turn a clean furrow in forest soil skittered over the surface of the prairie sod like a pebble skipping across a pond. Prairie soils seemed to be mostly roots.

Breaking prairie sod became a business. Men traveled the settlements with heavy plows pulled by several teams of oxen and hired out to plow land at so much an acre. The sound of the tearing roots, they said, was like the rattle of small arms fire, as if an infantry company was engaged in battle. Individual farmers couldn't plow the prairie until 1837 when an Illinois blacksmith named John Deere invented the steel moldboard plow.

EVOLUTION OF THE PRAIRIE

Prairies are grasslands. The dominant plants are grasses—although many other kinds of plants are present. The group of plants we call grasses evolved during the Miocene Epoch, a period that began about 25 million years ago. Grasses have since become the dominant vegetation over large areas of the earth. The prairies of North America, the pampas of South America, the steppes of Central Asia, and the plains of East Africa are all grasslands.

Grasslands develop on flat lands in areas where long periods without rainfall are common—although the climate is not as dry as it is in deserts. These periods of drought may be regular seasonal occurrences—like the dry seasons of tropical lands—or they may happen only in some years—like the summer droughts of the American Midwest.

Those periodic droughts and the flat ground that offers few obstacles to advancing flames have made fire a major force in the ecology of the world's grasslands. Millions of years of evolution in the presence of fire have

Blazing star and goldenrod create a colorful display in a mid-summer prairie. The flower show starts in spring and continues until October.

HISTORIC RANGE OF THE PRAIRIE

Little remains east of the Mississippi, but some of the biggest and best of the surviving remnants are in the Chicago region.

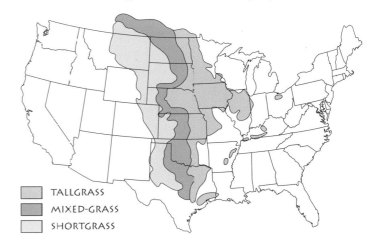

TALLGRASS
MIXED-GRASS
SHORTGRASS

made the tallgrass prairie dependent on periodic fires for its survival.

The prairies of central North America form a triangle extending from the foothills of the Rockies on the west to Ohio on the east. In the Chicago Wilderness, the prairies share the land with a variety of wooded communities. To the west, trees become more rare. On the high plains in the shadow of the Rocky Mountains, they grow only in narrow strips along the rivers.

The western prairies—the grasslands of eastern Montana, Wyoming, and Colorado, are considered short-grass prairies. Precipitation averages less than 20 inches a year. In the dry, windy environment, plants hug the ground, seldom growing much above a foot in height. With increasing precipitation, the grasses and other

prairie plants get taller. From central Nebraska east, tall-grass prairies dominate the treeless parts of the landscape. Early accounts tell of grasses tall enough to hide a man on horseback. That height must have been rare, but settlers often lost cattle in the pastures of August

ROOTS AND SOILS

Most of the biomass, the living material, of both prairie grasses and prairie wildflowers—botanists call them forbs—is underground. On deep soils, the root systems of some prairie species extend nearly 20 feet below the surface. They may live for decades, each spring sending up new green shoots to flower, set seed, and die.

1 *Side-oats grama grass,* **2** *Prairie dropseed,* **3** *Whorled milkweed,* **4** *Purple prairie clover,* **5** *Gray goldenrod,* **6** *False boneset,* **7** *Tall boneset,* **8** *Hoary vervain,* **9** *Cylindric blazingstar,* **10** *Daisy fleabane,* **11** *Little bluestem,* **12** *Indian grass,* **13** *Rough blazingstar,* **14** *Round-headed bush-clover,* **15** *Stiff goldenrod,* **16** *Compass plant,* **17** *Big bluestem,* **18** *Wild quinine,* **19** *Rattlesnake master,* **20** *Culver's root,* **21** *Wild onion,* **22** *Flowering spurge,* **23** *White wild indigo,* **24** *Yellow-headed coneflower,* **25** *Canada goldenrod,* **26** *Prairie dock,* **27** *Switchgrass,* **28** *Obedient plant,* **29** *New England aster,* **30** *Saw-toothed sunflower,* **31** *Tall goldenrod,* **32** *Smooth white lettuce,* **33** *Mountain mint,* **34** *Canada wi'd rye,* **35** *Stiff gentian,* **36** *Closed gentian,* **37** *Fringed gentian,* **38** *Prairie blazingstar,* **39** *Cordgrass,* **40** *Blue flag iris,* **41** *Reddish bulrush,* **42** *Common cattail*

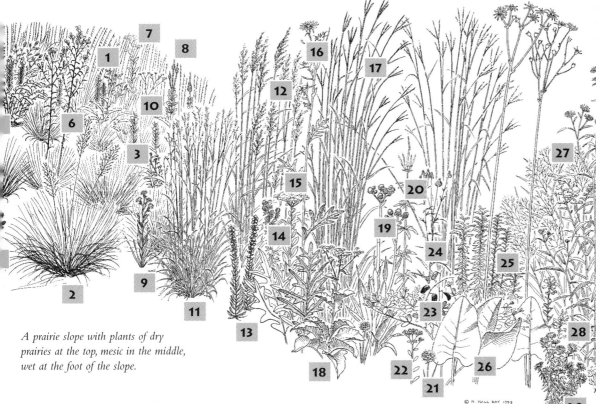

A prairie slope with plants of dry prairies at the top, mesic in the middle, wet at the foot of the slope.

© N. HALL DAY 1993

Dr. Robert F. Betz
of Northeastern Illinois University led campaign to save Indian Boundary Prairies; initiated first large scale prairie restoration at Fermi National Accelerator Lab near Batavia, Illinois.

These huge root systems are constantly growing and constantly dying. New roots seek new sources of minerals and water in the subsoil. Old roots die and decay, adding organic matter to the soil.

Organic matter may form a layer nearly two feet thick in prairie soils. It is this organic matter that gives prairie soils their dark color. Organic matter also made prairie soils extremely productive of crops such as corn and soybeans. This fertility doomed nearly all the prairies.

TYPES OF PRAIRIES

As many as 350 different species of plants grew on the prairies of Illinois, Indiana, and Wisconsin, but they didn't all grow together. Instead they grew in distinctive communities. Each community had its own unique mix of species. Soil moisture and soil texture are the two most important factors in controlling where these communities grew. Prairies on wet soils shared many plants with such wetland communities as sedge meadows and fens. Prairies on sandy soils, where the coarse soil texture lets water drain away quickly after rains, often contained plants more common in the drier lands to the west.

Ecologists have named five moisture groups: wet, wet-mesic, mesic, dry-mesic and dry. The

A line of life-giving fire blows across a prairie in the Chicago Wilderness. Fires are essential to the health of this ecosystem.

word "mesic"—which means "in the middle" or "moderate"—turns up often in ecology. In addition, two kinds of prairies are classified by the texture of the ground they grow in. Sand prairies grow along Lake Michigan and inland as well. Gravel hill prairies often grow on top of kames.

If we survey the plants growing in a wet prairie, we are likely to find that cordgrass (*Spartina pectinata*) and blue joint grass (*Calamagrostis canadensis*) are the most common grasses. In dry prairies, side-oats grama (*Bouteloua curtipendula*) becomes important. In mesic prairies, the dominant grasses are big bluestem (*Andropogon gerardii*) and northern dropseed (*Sporobolus heterolepis*). The forbs show similar shifts.

PRAIRIES AND FIRE

Prairies are fire-dependent communities. Without fire, tallgrass prairies are invaded by trees and shrubs that kill the prairie plants with their shade. Without fire, species begin to vanish from the prairie. Smaller plants and plants with small seeds seem to go first. Legumes also disappear. Their removal makes it easier for weeds to invade.

Some trees can survive regular prairie fires. Bur oak (*Quercus macrocarpa*) and black oak (*Quercus velutina*) can live for a century or more even though regular fires repeatedly kill all parts of the plant that are above ground. They survive as roots—called "grubs." The grubs are not harmed by the fires and each year, they produce new sprouts. When large scale settlement began, people noticed communities they called "brushy prairies." These were prairies where bur oak, black oak, and sometimes white oak grubs were common. Fire suppression after settlement quickly turned these brushy prairies into oak woods.

Prairie remnants are scattered over the Chicago region. Most of the prairies shown on this map are less than 20 acres.

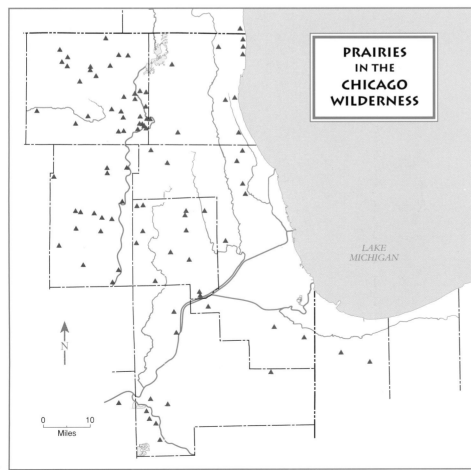

PRAIRIES
IN THE
CHICAGO
WILDERNESS

LAKE
MICHIGAN

N

0   10
Miles

New growth sprouts with the help of minerals released by fire.

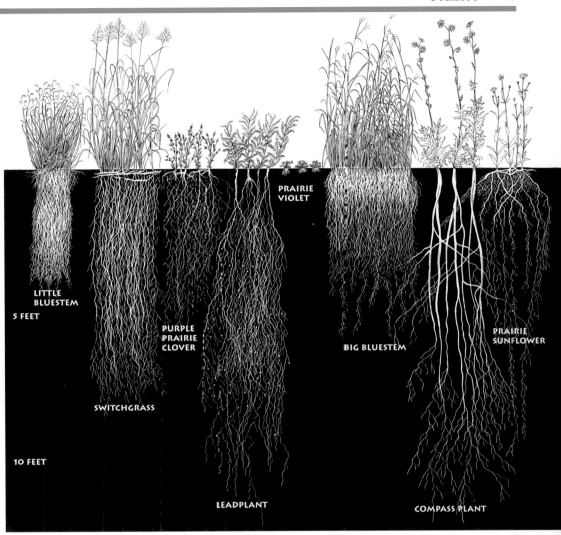

Most of the living stuff in a prairie is underground. The huge root systems of prairie plants live for many years, sending up new green shoots every year. The death of old roots adds humus to the soil.

Historical accounts tell us that Native Americans set fires every year to improve forage for bison and elk. If the weather was right, these fires might burn for days.

Fires burn best on level ground. In hills, they burn well uphill but are likely to go out on downhill slopes. In the Chicago Wilderness, prairies dominated the flat land unless that land was on the downwind side of a river, lake, or other permanent body of water. Fires burning from west to east often went out on the west banks of river or the western shores of lakes and permanent wetlands.

PRAIRIE SUCCESSION

In the presence of fire, prairies are very stable communities. Many of the common prairie plants live for many years, but they do not readily invade new ground. Before settlement, disturbed places--like buffalo wallows would be quickly filled with weedy prairie species— plants that grow fast and specialize in invading disturbed ground. In time, the more conservative species would replace these invaders.

During the past 175 years, millions of acres of tall-grass prairies have been converted to cornfields or covered with buildings. Surviving prairies are small and widely scattered. It is impossible for seeds from these small prairies to reach all the lands where they could grow.

With the native prairie species so rare, a cornfield left idle for a few years is likely to be invaded by plants from Europe and Asia that have been imported into this area since settlement. Most of the grasslands in the Chicago Wilderness are dominated by exotic (non-native) species such as Hungarian brome grass (*Bromus inermis*) and Queen Anne's lace (*Daucus carota*).

The tall-grass prairie survives in tiny fragments. Conservationists have mounted protracted campaigns on behalf of prairie remnants of five or ten acres. Hope for the survival of this ecosystem rest on good management of these fragments and on restoration projects that return prairie to lands where it has not grown for a century or more. The Midewin National Tall-grass Prairie in Will County, the largest restoration ever undertaken, will someday soon return the bison to the Illinois prairie.

VIOLA PEDATIFIDA
Prairie violet

POTENTILLA ARGUTA
Prairie cinquefoil

SISYRINCHIUM ALBIDUM
Common blue-eyed grass

POTENTILLA SIMPLEX
Common cinquefoil

ZIZIA APTERA
Heart-leaved meadow parsnip

PHLOX PILOSA
Prairie phlox

HEUCHERA RICHARDSONII
Prairie alum root

TRADESCANTIA OHIENSIS
Common spiderwort

FRAGARIA VIRGINIANA
Wild strawberry

The Beauty of

Imagine a circle the size of a hula hoop. All 30 of the plants pictured on these two pages were found growing in just such a circle randomly placed at the Somme Prairie Nature Preserve in Northbrook, Illinois. Biodiversity is typical of tallgrass prairie. If we studied a few acres of prairie, we might find a hundred species of plants.

In our hoop, the violets bloom first. Their flowers open in late April. From that point until the moment in October when the last aster fades, something would always be blooming inside this small circle. A bumble bee in search of pollen, a butterfly looking for nectar would stand a good chance of finding what it needs.

LITHOSPERMUM CANESCENS
Hoary puccoon

SMILACINA STELLATA
Starry false solomon's seal

**VIOLA PAPILIONACEA
(VIOLA AFFINIS)**
LeConte's violet

PARTHENIUM INTEGRIFOLIUM
Wild quinine

ERYNGIUM YUCCIFOLIUM
Rattlesnake master

COMANDRA UMBELLATA
False toad flax

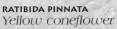

SORGHASTRUM NUTANS
Indian grass

RATIBIDA PINNATA
Yellow coneflower

CAREX CONOIDEA
Prairie gray sedge

CAREX BICKNELLII
Copper-shouldered oval sedge

ASTER ERICOIDES
Heath aster

ALLIUM CANADENSE
Wild onion

Biodiversity

Several species of the tiny butterflies called skippers could reproduce in our hoop. Skipper caterpillars feed on grasses and sedges. On the violets, we might find caterpillars that would grow into gaudy orange and black fritillaries.

In healthy ecosystems, energy flows freely through the system. There are many pathways for it to follow. Plants of many species support a variety of insects. Snakes, salamanders, and meadowlarks eat the insects and northern harriers eat the insect eaters. Thanks to the biodiversity in our hoop, the flow of energy can support them all.

ASTER NOVAE-ANGLIAE
New England aster

LIATRIS SPICATA
Marsh blazing star

SOLIDAGO JUNCEA
Early goldenrod

ANDROPOGON SCOPARIUS
Little bluestem grass

LIATRIS ASPERA
Rough blazing star

SILPHIUM TEREBINTHINACEUM
Prairie dock

AGROPYRON TRACHYCAULUM
Bearded wheatgrass

BROMUS KALMII
Kalm's brome

ASTER AZUREUS
Sky-blue aster

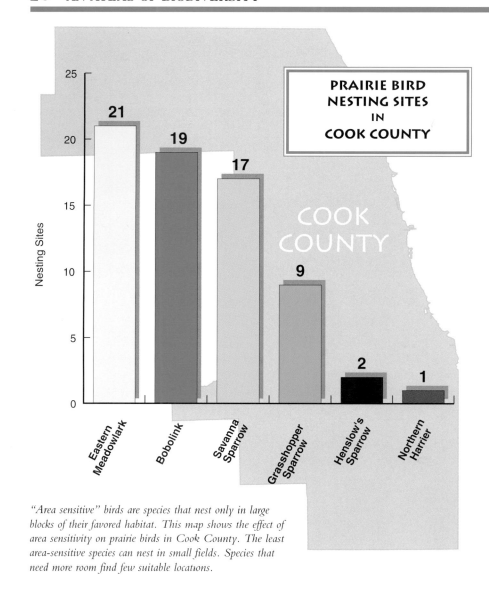

**PRAIRIE BIRD
NESTING SITES
IN
COOK COUNTY**

COOK COUNTY

"Area sensitive" birds are species that nest only in large blocks of their favored habitat. This map shows the effect of area sensitivity on prairie birds in Cook County. The least area-sensitive species can nest in small fields. Species that need more room find few suitable locations.

Threatened in the state, the upland sandpiper's largest Illinois population is on the Midewin National Tallgrass Prairie in Will County.

Dickcissels are wanderers. They change nesting grounds from year to year.

PRAIRIES
Birds

On the green prairies of early summer, early in the morning before the sun burns off the dew, you might hear a long eerie whistling cry as if the wind were alive and singing.

From overhead comes a tinkling song, a long complex toccata delivered from high in the sky. These are songs of prairie birds. The cry comes from the upland sandpiper (*Bartramia longicauda*). The toccata is the flight song of the bobolink (*Dolichonyx oryzivorus*).

Many grassland birds have taken to singing in the air. With no trees to serve as perches, they provide their own elevated stages to spread their songs over the prairie.

The tallgrass prairie supports a distinctive group of birds. Adapted to life in a treeless environment, they sing in the air or from swaying perchs on the stems of prairie grasses and build their nests on the ground.

Most are migratory, but a few species have found ways to survive prairie winters. The cold winds are a severe test, but those same winds serve to keep some areas free of snow, revealing food for the resident birds.

Meadowlarks are partial migrants; some birds go south, but a few remain through the winter. We have two species: the eastern (*Sternella magna*) and the western (*S. neglecta*).

Meadow larks eat a varied diet, specializing in insects in summer; switching to seeds in winter. They are perhaps the least area sensitive of our prairie birds. Area sensitivity refers to the need which many birds have for large blocks of uniform habitat around their nesting territories. The Henslow's sparrow (*Ammodramus henslowii*), another prairie species, claims a territory of only a few acres, but it rarely nests in any grassland smaller than about 80 acres. Meadowlarks can nest in fields as small as 20 acres, and they often sing from tree limbs at the edge of fields. The discovery of area sensitivity has made us aware of the need for large preserves to sustain all our species.

Upland sandpipers and bobolinks are the champion long-distance migrants among our

Once extirpated from the Chicago Wilderness Region, sandhill cranes are breeding once again in Lake, McHenry, and DuPage Counties.

Grasshopper sparrows use only a small space for nesting territory, but they will not nest on small patches of grassland.

prairie birds. They fly all the way to Argentina for the winter. Dickcissels (*Spiza americana*) winter as far south as Venezuela. This species is known for its nomadic habits. It may nest in some numbers in a location one year, be completely absent the next year, only to return in subsequent years. These movements may be triggered by changes in food availability. They may also be affected by moisture differences. In dry years, birds of mesic prairie may move into usually wet prairies and in wet years, birds of wet prairies may seek out normally mesic sites.

Northern harriers (*Circus cyaneus*) and short-eared owls (*Asio flammeus*) are the principal hunters of the prairie. They seek their prey, rodents, small birds, herps, and insects by flying low over the ground and pouncing on anything that shows itself. Both of these birds favor wetter prairies and often hunt over places we would class as wetlands. The former name for the harrier was "marsh hawk."

Sandhill cranes (*Grus canadensis*) also occupy both wet prairies and marshes, sedge meadows, and other wetlands.

Birds are most affected by the structure of their habitat. Prairie species nest quite successfully in meadows filled with Eurasian grasses imported into the Midwest in the past 175 years. As long as a place has little or no woody vegetation, the prairie birds will continue to use it.

Their ability to adapt to life among strange grasses helped sustain high populations of prairie birds even after agriculture had destroyed almost all the prairies. The birds simply moved into pastures and hay fields. Birds such as the upland sandpiper that prefer shorter grass actually benefited from the change. However, the switch from general farming to an almost exclusive reliance on corn and soybeans produced a disaster for prairie birds. Since the 1950s, populations have declined 90 percent or more for all our prairie species.

Today, the prairie birds that remain almost all nest in meadows of Eurasian grasses. Few of our prairie remnants are large enough to support bird populations. The song of the bobolink is heard only on a few of the larger sites.

PRAIRIES
Butterflies and Moths

This recently discovered moth of the genus Papaipema lives on prairie remnants in the Chicago Wilderness. It has not yet received a scientific name.

Most of the animals on earth are insects, so it is not surprising that most of the animals of the prairie are insects. In the Chicago Wilderness region, this is more true than it ought to be. Our prairie remnants are mostly so small that they can't support any animals larger than insects. Even our prairie sparrows usually have to make do with fields full of imported grasses and weeds because our real prairies are so tiny.

With prairies so scarce, the continued survival of thousands of species of insects could be in doubt. Small populations of any plant or animal are always in danger of being wiped out by weather or disease or some other catastrophe, and with prairies so widely scattered, the odds against a prairie being colonized by new individuals of the deceased species are very long.

If insects are like prairie birds, able to adapt to life amid imported species, then we need not worry particularly about their futures. As long as there are weed patches around, the insects can thrive. But what if insects are like white-

Ants tend the caterpillar of the silvery blue butterfly.

That means that more than 200 species could not continue to live in our area if the last prairie and savanna remnants were destroyed.

Remnant dependence is particularly high among butterflies and moths, with 40 percent of our local grassland butterflies confined to prairies.

Among root-borer moths of the genus *Papaipema*, more than 80 percent of our local species are confined to remnants of the natural landscape. One species of these moths, *Papaipema eryngia,* lives only in the roots of rattlesnake master (*Eryngium yuccifolium*), a plant common on prairies but rarely seen outside them. This moth is known from only three sites in the world: two here in the Chicago region and one in Oklahoma.

It is not surprising that a large number of butterflies would be dependent on particular plant communities, since caterpillars are often dependent on particular plants as food sources. The degree of specialization varies, but it is always present. Some caterpillars are confined to a single species, others to a single genus, still others to a single family.

Skippers are tiny butterflies whose caterpillars feed on grasses.

This aphrodite fritillary (Speyeria aphrodite) is a prairie specialist. It does not live on grasslands of Eurasian plants.

fringed orchids and the other conservative prairie species that survive only in prairie communities? We could be facing the wholesale extinction of an entire fauna.

Extended investigation into more than 800 species belonging to seven families of insects of prairies and savannas has revealed that about one quarter of the total species in these groups are confined to remnants of the native landscape.

When Marquette and Joliet passed through the Chicago Region in 1673 they wrote of the "wild cattle" and "stags" that could be seen grazing on the prairies. They were referring, of course, to bison (*Bison bison*) and elk (*Cervus elaphus*), the largest of our native animals.

Bison were the first large animals to be killed off following settlement, and elk followed shortly thereafter. Cows and horses became the major grazing animals on the rapidly shrinking prairie.

Grazing animals have definite tastes in food plants. It is possible to tell whether a field has been grazed by cattle or horses just by looking at what has been eaten and what has been left alone. We may soon have a chance to learn what effect bison and elk have on a prairie. Current plans call for reintroducing these animals at the Midewin National Tallgrass Prairie in Will County.

Big Grazers

Bison were probably the first animals extirpated from this region after settlement. They may soon be reintroduced at Midewin National Tallgrass Prairie.

Herps

People who study reptiles and amphibians are called herpetologists. The name comes from a Greek word meaning "creeping." Herpetologists call the creeping creatures they study "herps." It is a useful word, short and easy to remember, and it saves us from the endless repetition of the cumbersome phrase "reptiles and amphibians." We will use "herps" to refer to these animals throughout this Atlas.

The Chicago Region is rich in garter snakes. We are at the eastern end of the range of the plains garter snake (*Thamnophis radix*). A few isolated populations of the western ribbon snake (*Thamnophis proximus*) and northern ribbon snake (*Thamnophis sauritus septentrionalis*) can be found in our region. We even have our own special garter snake, the Chicago garter snake (*Thamnophis sirtalis semifasciatus*) a subspecies of the eastern garter snake.

In the chaotic conditions of a booming metropolis, you might discover one of these snakes almost anywhere, but in places where natural conditions are a bit more stable, they begin to sort themselves out. At the Fermi National Accelerator Lab near Batavia, IL, a large scale ecological restoration project has been underway for more than 20 years. Inside the accelerator ring, an enormous half-buried steel doughnut a mile in diameter, is a small

grove of oaks surrounded by a recovering prairie. Search among the oak trees and you will probably find *sirtalis*, the eastern garter snake. Out on the prairie, the usual snake is *radix*. Search a transition zone, the land within about 200 yards of the trees, and you might find either species. The snakes are a walking—or rather slithering—demonstration of the need to protect all the varieties of natural habitat in our region.

Herps can serve as guides to conditions on the land. Their limited mobility makes it difficult for them to travel in search of a better home, especially in a land of six-lane expressways. As a result, they are vulnerable to local extinction. If a small population dies out, new animals of the same species are unlikely to be able to colonize the vacated habitat.

The Smooth Green Snake

In the Chicago Region, the herp most closely associated with the prairie is the smooth green snake, a lovely little serpent whose smoothly scaly skin practically glows with a Kelly green tint. The presence of a smooth green snake (Opheodrys vernalis) can be taken as an indication of the quality of a prairie remnant. Found in an old field full of recently imported Eurasian weeds, the smooth green snake is a sign that the land was once a prairie, and that it has not been too heavily dosed with pesticides.

Smooth green snakes are small. The largest specimen ever measured was 26 inches long. Their diet is principally insects.

WOODED COMMUNITIES

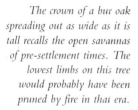

Pillars of Mighty Cathedral Aisles

The crown of a bur oak spreading out as wide as it is tall recalls the open savannas of pre-settlement times. The lowest limbs on this tree would probably have been pruned by fire in that era.

Marsh marigolds (Caltha palustris) brighten spring days in wet forests and flatwoods in Chicago Wilderness.

Trees in Chicago Wilderness once grew as lone sentinels on the prairie. They grew in open groves and sun-dappled woodlands where they sometimes attained the noble shapes that reminded visitor Ellen Fuller of cathedral pillars 150 years ago.

These wooded communities varied over time and space. They blended into each other on their borders. The categories we have created to describe them are only rough descriptions of nature.

Climate, soils, topography, and drainage set limits on the kinds of natural communities that can live in our region. Other forces shape the landscape within the limits created by these factors. In our landscape, in the thousands of years before large-scale settlement, fire was the most important shaping force.

In those times it was the frequency and intensity of fire that determined whether a given piece of ground would be an open grove or a dense forest. We can arrange the pre-settlement wooded communities on a shade gradient, and when we make such a division, we find that our shade gradient is also a fire gradient. The more open communities grew in places where fires came often and burned with some intensity. Shadier places saw fewer fires or less intense fires. Some of our dense forests are fire sensitive

communities that could live only where fires were rare events.

Our sunniest places were prairies where no trees grew. The next community on our gradient is the savanna. Savannas are considered grasslands with some trees. Ample sun reaches the ground, promoting the growth of a heavy turf of grasses and wildflowers that is fuel for fires.

Our open woodlands are some of the most distinctive communities in the region. Here grew white oaks (*Quercus alba*), bur oaks (*Quercus macrocarpa*), and red oaks (*Quercus rubra*), along with shagbark hickory (*Carya ovata*), bitternut hickory (*Carya cordiformis*), and black walnut (*Juglans nigra*). The understory in these woods was equally varied. Some had thickets of shrubs like American hazel (*Corylus americana*) and wild plum (*Prunus americana*). Other forests were open enough to allow farmers to drive a team and wagon through them. The species of trees in these woods were adapted to frequent fire. The canopy was open enough to allow oak seedlings and saplings to grow.

Our dense forests included some communities where fire was still a factor. At the heart of many prairie groves were stands of red oak (*Quercus rubra*) and black maple (*Acer nigrum*). And small areas had communities dominated by sugar maple (*Acer saccharum*) and basswood (*Tilia*

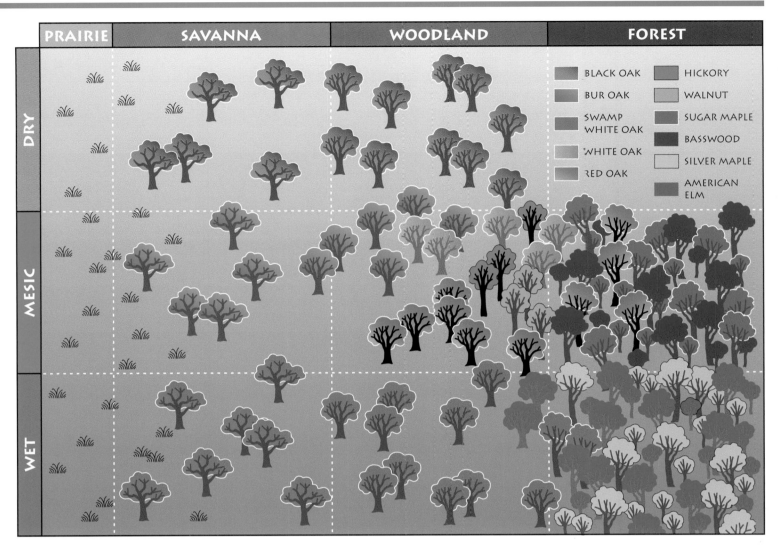

| PRAIRIE | SAVANNA | WOODLAND | FOREST |

BLACK OAK   HICKORY
BUR OAK   WALNUT
SWAMP WHITE OAK   SUGAR MAPLE
WHITE OAK   BASSWOOD
RED OAK   SILVER MAPLE
AMERICAN ELM

DRY   MESIC   WET

americana) where fire played little or no role.

We can also divide our wooded communities into categories based on soil moisture. In our region moisture conditions for plants are mainly affected by soil texture and drainage.

The classifications scientists use to describe natural communities give a short, simple name to a very complicated thing. When we talk of "oak savannas" or "oak-hickory forests," we are referring to communities that may include hundreds of species of plants, and—when you add up all the beetles, spiders, snails, and centipedes—thousands of species of animals. When we study a real natural area and decide what communities are present, we look at the entire biota, all the living things. Overall differences in the biota tell ecologists whether a given community developed as an open woodland or a dense forest. The biota also help us identify communities that have been seriously harmed by the changes that large-scale settlement has brought.

All of our wooded communities have been changed by the altered conditions that have followed settlement. The suppression of fire, in particular, has had a profound effect. With fire gone from the community, fire sensitive trees

such as box elders (Acer negundo), ashes (Fraxinus spp.) and sugar maples have moved into oak forests, open woodlands, and savannas, places where they could not survive when fire was an active force.

These trees cast a dense shade. If we looked only at the amount of shade, we might today identify a remnant open woodland or a savanna as a dense forest. But if we look at the more conservative plants and animals, those most tied to a particular community, we see herps and wildflowers typical of open woodlands. The biggest and oldest trees are white and bur oaks, open woodland trees.

All these things tell us we are not looking at land that was originally a dense forest; we are looking at a savanna or open woodland undergoing a process of decay. The species that live in these communities, the species that with their combined activities create these communities are dying out. Thousands of years of history in this place and millions of years of evolutionary history are dying with them. Only a poor mix of a few trees, some weeds and much bare ground remains. Fortunately restoration can reverse this trend.

WOODED COMMUNITIES IN THE CHICAGO WILDERNESS

This diagram arranges the pre-settlement wooded communities of this region on two axes. One separates them according to soil moisture from wet to dry and the other according to the density of the tree canopy. This density gradient is also a fire gradient. Fires burned hotter and more often in the communities to the left of the diagram. Communities to the right saw fewer fires.

WOODED COMMUNITIES
Savannas

Swamp white oaks and pin oaks (Quercus palustris) shade the wet savanna while tall joe pye weed (Eupatorium maculatum) brightens late summer with its purple flowers.

Black oaks are the most common trees in the sand savannas.

Bur Oak

Bur oaks (Quercus macrocarpa) are the most common trees of the Midwestern mesic savanna groves. Their thick, corky bark helped the large trees survive intense fires. Even fires hot enough to kill the above-ground parts of the tree could not harm the roots. Dormant buds at the base of the dead trunk could spring to life and produce new stems. Enormous root masses called grubs grew over the years. With these well-established root systems feeding them water and nutrients, the young stems needed only a few years without fire to grow tall enough to get their crowns above the flames, giving them a good chance of surviving fires. Concentrations of bur oaks in the Chicago Wilderness often mark places where fire was frequent in the past. The heart of this species' range is in the savanna region of the Midwest.

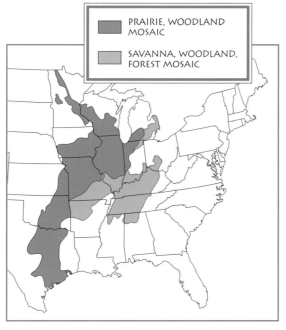

PRAIRIE, WOODLAND
MOSAIC

SAVANNA, WOODLAND,
FOREST MOSAIC

Savanna trees have broad crowns, an indication that they grew in places where they had space to spread out. Some old savanna oaks are as wide as they are tall.

Sand savannas grow on dunes along Lake Michigan and inland on sandy soils. Black oaks (*Quercus velutina*) are the dominant trees in these savannas, although white pine (*Pinus strobus*) and jack pine (*Pinus banksiana*) are part of this community in the Indiana Dunes. The understory of the sand savanna is mainly species typical of dry prairies.

The sandy soils of the sand savanna create a dry environment that makes it easier for fires to burn through them. However, these soils have very low fertility. Because of this low fertility, the annual production of new leaves, stems, and twigs is small. Low productivity means there is little fuel for fires, so when fires do break out, they are likely to be small.

The ability of oaks to resprout from their roots after the above ground parts of the tree have been killed by fire is one of the reasons they are able to thrive in fire-dependent communties such as savannas. Resprouts often grow into trees with two or more trunks rising from one root system.

Wet savannas grow on land with a subsoil of clay that prevents water from draining away. Standing water may be present in spring and early summer, but by autumn, the ground is dry enough to allow a fire to burn through the grove. Swamp white oaks (*Quercus bicolor*) are the most common trees.

The major tree of the mesic savanna is the bur oak (*Quercus macrocarpa*), our most nearly fireproof local tree. Bur oak savannas occupy silt-loam soils as well as gravel soils.

Bur oak savannas have nearly vanished. Grazing killed off much of the understory and fire suppression allowed fire sensitive trees and shrubs to invade. These cast enough shade to prevent the oaks from reproducing.

The understory in these savannas was either graminoid—which means dominated by grasses—or shrubby. American hazel (*Corylus americana*) and wild plum (*Prunus americana*), which can both grow in areas with moderate fire regimes, were typical shrubs.

Open Woodlands

The open woodlands of the Chicago region were one of the most distinctive and diverse community types in our native landscape. Oaks, as a group, were the most common trees in these woodlands, but the exact composition of the community was quite varied.

On mesic soils—places where soil moisture lay between the extremes of wet and dry—combinations of oaks and hickories (*Carya spp.*) might be found. Mixed oak woods where bur oak, white oak, and scarlet oak (*Quercus coccinea*) grew together were also present. Smaller amounts of black cherry (*Prunus serotina*) might also be present, but the thin bark of this species leaves it vulnerable to fire.

Trees in open woodlands grow much closer together than savanna trees, and their crowns are correspondingly narrower. However, enough light reaches down to the lower trunks to allow branches to grow low on the trees.

The presence of fire in open woodlands prevents invasive species such as ashes and sugar maples from taking over the community, and the open quality lets in enough light to permit the oaks to reproduce and maintain themselves as the principal trees.

In the native landscape, when healthy open woodlands could be found throughout the region, these communities were home to some spectacular concentrations of wildlife. The many nutbearing trees—oaks, hickories, and walnuts—along with the presence of American hazel (*Corylus americana*) shrubs in the understory, provided rich food sources for the now-extinct passenger pigeon (*Ectopistes migratorius*) and for wild turkeys (*Meleagris gallopavo*) as well. The latter species has been extirpated from this region, but could be reintroduced.

In the understory, plants typical of the open woodlands include yellow pimpernel (*Taenidia integerrima*), a species that might be found in border zones between woodlands and prairies. Wild hyacinths (*Camassia scilloides*) grow in woodlands and savannas.

Our open woodlands have been hit especially hard by the changes settlement has brought. In addition to invasions by native trees, this community has been especially vulnerable to the exotic invading shrub called common buckthorn (*Rhamnus cathartica*). The conditions of medium shade seem ideal for this species. Buckthorn and the native invaders create such dense shade that they kill the understory plants and effectively prevent the oaks from reproducing.

In recent years, restoration and management, including prescribed burnings, have revived many open woodlands. Typical understory plants have returned, and oaks are beginning to reproduce again.

Open oak woodlands with rich understories are one of the natural wonders of Chicago Wilderness.

Black Maples and Sugar Maples

Botanists still argue about the differences between black maples (Acer nigrum) and sugar maples (Acer saccharum). The two species appear quite similar in many important respects, and some specimens today show characteristics of both. Older trees are more distinctive, and in the pre-settlement landscape, they behaved in quite distinctive ways. Sugar maples were confined to places where fire almost never came, while black maples could be found in forests and woodlands where fire was a regular occurrence. Black maple would have been the more common species then and the major local source of maple sugar.

In dense forests, most wildflowers bloom in early spring before the trees leaf out. In woodlands such as the one shown here, more light reaches the ground and more flowers bloom in mid and late summer.

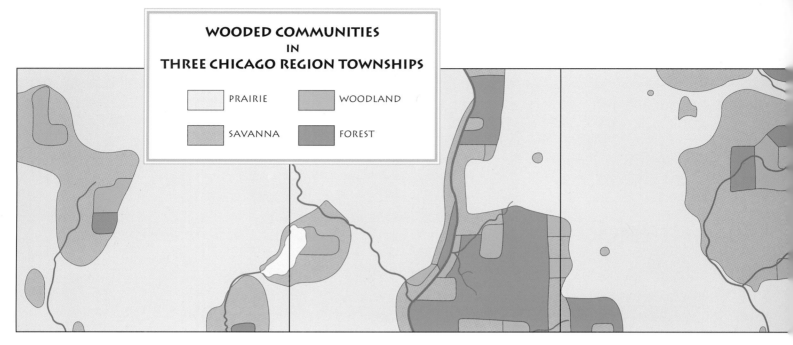

WOODED COMMUNITIES
IN
THREE CHICAGO REGION TOWNSHIPS

PRAIRIE WOODLAND

SAVANNA FOREST

This map of the presettlement vegetation in three townships in eastern Kane and western DuPage County shows the effects of fire on the distribution of wooded communities. Prairie areas on the map are on flat glacial outwash. Wooded areas are on moraines where hills give fires a patchy distribution. Land east of rivers and Nelson Lake Marsh was relatively protected from fire. The most fire-sensitive community, a mesic forest, grew on the east bank of the Fox River.

WOODED COMMUNITIES
Flatwoods

Early spring is wet in the flatwoods.

Flatwoods communities are a product of topography and the complex, multi-layered deposits left by the glaciers. They develop on land that is flat or gently sloping. Below the surface, usually between 24 and 36 inches deep, is a layer of clay that restricts the movement of water down into the ground.

This clay layer is not the virtually waterproof hardpan found under southern flatwoods, but the clay is enough of a barrier to force water to move laterally rather than down. Most of the time, the soil above the clay layer is saturated, and the water moves in sheets over the surface.

During spring and early summer, water may stand on the surface in puddles and shallow ponds. By late summer, both the surface and the soils above the clay layer, may be completely dry. Small knolls may support plants typical of dry situations, while wetland species grow in the low places.

Fire played a major role in determining just what sort of community developed in this wet/dry situation, but long term fire suppression has made it difficult for us to gauge the extent of fire's effects. Pin oak (*Quercus palustris*) is now frequent in flatwoods, but fire may have kept its numbers down in the past. Other common species are swamp white oak (*Quercus bicolor*) and various ashes (*Fraxinus spp.*), especially black ash (*Fraxinus nigra*). Huge old bur oaks are a feature of some flatwoods. The absence

of fire has also allowed silver maple (*Acer saccharinum*) to become common.

It is likely that in presettlement time when fires were frequent, flatwoods were more open and savanna-like than they are now. The change in tree density can lead to changes in the plants of the understory. Open flatwoods share many ground layer plants with sedge meadows. Fire-starved flatwoods are often too shady for such species. Fire-starved flatwoods also contain some of the largest and most vigorous specimens of poison ivy (*Rhus radicans*) in our region. The vines climb to the sky by clinging to the trunks of the largest trees.

Forests

White trilliums (Trillium grandiflorum) bloom in early spring in an oak forest in Chicago Wilderness.

Dense forests were rather rare in the native landscape of the Chicago region. Probably the most common type, the black maple—red oak forest was adapted to periodic fires.

Our forests were sometimes found along rivers or in sheltered ravines near the shore of Lake Michigan where the topography inhibited fires.

At the eastern edge of our region, the American beech (*Fagus grandifolium*), one of the dominant trees in the forests of the eastern states, reaches the western edge of its range. Other prominent species of the beech-maple forest—trees, shrubs, and understory herbs, grasses, and ferns—also are not found west of Porter County, Indiana. A community that dominates much of the landscape to the east is here more like our fens and bogs. It was confined to islands where special circumstances made things suitable for it to grow.

Climate differences may be involved in these changes and soils play a role too, but fire seems to be the major factor. The dominant trees of the eastern forest have little resistance to fire. In the Chicago Wilderness, oak woodlands and savannas grow on lands that would be covered with beech-maple forests just a few miles to the east.

Our floodplain forests are poorly understood, and few high quality examples exist. Silver maple (*Acer saccharinum*) is a dominant species in this forest, growing along with ashes (*Fraxinus spp.*). Before Dutch elm disease struck, American elm (*Ulmus americana*) was an important species in this community.

The groundlayer today is often rather sparse. However, this may represent a post-settlement condition. Because our sewer and drainage systems direct so much water into our rivers immediately after rains, flooding patterns are quite different than they were before settlement. Other changes in these communities may be involved as well.

Fire suppression has allowed trees of the floodplain forests to invade upland sites where they did not grow prior to settlement. Swamps, forested areas that stay wet year around, are absent from the Illinois portion of the Chicago Wilderness. They do occur at the Indiana Dunes. Red maple (*Acer rubrum*) is a major species in these swamps.

Fungi

Fungi play three major roles in ecosystems. They are decomposers that break down dead tissue and release nutrients in the tissue for reuse in the system. They are disease-bearers—Dutch elm disease, for example, is caused by a fungus. And they grow on plant roots and help plants absorb nutrients from the soil. These mycorrhizzal (the word means "root-fungus") fungi absorb plant juices as food and deliver minerals to pay for their keep. In laboratory experiments, trees grown without mycorhizzal fungi are seriously stunted. The earth-star fungus (far right) is a decomposer. The ecology of the fungus at near-right is unknown. In Chicago Wilderness, our backyards may be as mysterious as the Amazon.

WOODED COMMUNITIES
Birds

Northern oriole

Scarlet tanager

Hairy woodpecker

Red-headed woodpecker

SAVANNA

PRAIRIE

WOODLAND

FOREST

Eastern bluebird

Ovenbird

THE BIRDS OF OUR WOODS

Birds respond to the structure of a community, nesting where tree density and size meet their needs. Within each community, they fill different niches based largely on what they eat and how and where they get their food. Woodpeckers look for insects in and on the bark of trees. They search mainly the trunk and larger limbs. They do not compete directly with insect-eating species that search chiefly among the leaves and small twigs in the crown of the tree or with ground feeding species. These divisions of the habitat allow large numbers of species to occupy the same grove of forest.

Birds are usually the most conspicuous animals in any wooded area. In nesting season, their songs are the most characteristic sound. Even in the dead of winter, resident birds sound their call notes as they search for food.

Some of our more common birds—robins, for example—nest wherever there are trees, from city parks and neighborhoods to dense forests. Most species are more specialized.

Birds tend to respond strongly to the structure of the plant community. The size of the trees and the density of tree growth affect bird populations far more than the presence or absence of any particular species of tree.

Northern (or Baltimore) orioles (*Icterus glabula*) favor open savanna groves. They have been able to adapt to the artificial savannas we create in parks. They build their hanging nests high in the crowns of tall trees.

Scarlet tanagers (*Piranga olivacea*), like the orioles, feed on insects and fruit. Orioles feed from the tree tops down to low shrubs, while tanagers do their foraging more exclusively in the crowns of trees. Scarlet tanagers prefer woodlands and forests where trees grow more densely than in savannas.

As a group, woodpeckers feed on the trunks and large limbs of trees. Their powerful beaks and heavy skulls allow them to dig through bark and wood to find beetle grubs and other insects that feed on the trees.

Hairy woodpeckers (*Picoides vilosus*) prefer dense forests and are more likely to be found in large blocks of forest rather than in small wood lots. Their smaller cousins, the downy woodpeckers (*Picoides pubescens*) live among young trees, and in open savanna groves.

Red-headed woodpeckers (*Melanerpes erythrocephalus*) are a species of open woods and groves. They seem to be subject to large population fluctuations. These may reflect the movement of birds to places where insect out-breaks have made food abundant. The closely related red-bellied woodpecker (*Melanerpes carolinus*) favors woodlands and forests. This species is near the northern edge of its range in our region and is more common in the southern half of the Chicago Wilderness.

The eastern bluebird (*Sialia sialis*) is a savanna species. It needs trees for nest sites—it nests in holes—but it feeds over open ground. Groves scattered across the prairie would be ideal habitat for this bird.

Down on the forest floor, the ovenbird (*Seiurus aurocapillus*) and the wood thrush (*Hylochichla mustelina*) search for insects amid the leaf litter. The ovenbird builds its nest on the ground, while the wood thrush nests in tall shrubs and small trees.

Wood thrushes are among the few species that might benefit from the invasion of our woodlands by common buckthorn, since the growth of more tall shrubs provides additional nesting sites. However, that modest benefit comes at the cost of heavy losses in other ani-

Gray squirrels do well in dense forests where food is hard to find.

Squirrels

W e have two species of squirrels in the Chicago region. One is the gray squirrel (*Sciurus carolinensis*) and the other is the fox squirrel (*Sciurus niger*).

The gray squirrel is mostly gray above, although highlights of buff and brown may show up on the back and head. The belly is white.

The fox squirrel is a bigger animal. Its underparts are rich foxy buff or ochre color, and its tail is richly colored with the same hue.

Scientists have a general consensus that in the pre-settlement landscape, fox squirrels were likely to be found in savannas and open woodlands. Gray squirrels were animals of the denser forests.

The red-tailed hawk is a savanna specialist.

mals and plants. Nesting success is also low, so these additional nests add few young to the population.

Cooper's hawk (*Accipiter cooperii*) is a bird-eating species that seems to favor open woodlands as nesting sites. It has recently been removed from the endangered list in Illinois.

The red-tailed hawk, (*Buteo jamaicensis*), our most common large raptor, is definitely a bird of the savannas. It builds its nest high in the trees, but it hunts by soaring over open fields. A landscape that mixes prairies and woodlands is ideal habitat for this bird.

This division may be an indicator of the relative importance of predators and the relative difficulty of finding food in the two kinds of habitat. The savannas and woodlands with their acorns, hickory nuts, and walnuts had lots of food, but they probably had many predators as well. Fox squirrels—by size and behavior better able to deal with predators than gray squirrels—could do well there.

The denser forests with fewer nut-bearing trees and sparser groundlayers rewarded food gatherers while predators were not common.

Until about 1950, fox squirrels were increasing in Illinois. Since then, a world of denser woods and fewer predators has seen gray squirrels increase and fox squirrels decline.

Fox squirrels do better in open woods and savannas where both food and predators are abundant.

WOODED COMMUNITIES
Herps

The larvae of a blue-spotted salamander has gills that allow it to live in the water of a vernal pond. Adults hunt on the forest floor.

Vernal ponds are temporary pools wet only in spring. They are essential breeding habitats for amphibians. Fish—major predators on eggs and tadpoles—cannot live in the temporary ponds.

Tiger salamaners are the most common salamander species in savannas. Their long maturation period requires ponds that stay wet well into the summer.

The forests and savannas of the Chicago region are rich in herps. In early spring, long before the leaves have emerged on the forest trees, the raspy, thumbnail-on-comb songs of the western chorus frog (*Pseudacris triseriata*) and the clear whistles of the spring peepers (*Pseudacris crucifer*) bring life to the dormant woods.

The salamanders of the forest floor do not call attention to themselves, but people lucky enough to be in the right place at the right time have seen hundreds at once.

The center of amphibian life in the spring woods is the vernal pond. The key characteristic of a vernal pond is that it exists for only part of the year. Formed of melting snow and early spring rain, it dries up during the summer. Its temporary nature makes it ideal for amphibians, because fish cannot live in it. In permanent bodies of water, fish become major predators on eggs, tadpoles, and salamander larvae, making life much more difficult for the herps.

SALAMANDERS

Eleven species of salamanders live in the Chicago region. Some of them are quite rare. The four-toed salamander (*Hemidactylium scuta-*

tum), a species fond of boggy places with sphagnum moss, is known from only a few locations. The Southern two-lined salamander (*Eurycea cirrigera*) and the smallmouth salamander (*Ambystoma texanum*) live only along the Kankakee River.

The three species most likely to be discovered in wooded areas in the Chicago region are the blue-spotted (*Ambystoma laterale*), the spotted (*Ambystoma maculatum*), and the tiger salamander (*Ambystoma tigrinum*).

All three of these species are called mole salamanders because they spend most of their time either underground or under something on the ground. Dead logs offer good cover as do the undersides of rocks. Herpetologists looking for animals sometimes leave a piece of plywood on the ground. Come back in a few days, and there may be a salamander under it. Rainy nights are the best time to see them out moving around, especially in very early spring when adults are heading for the breeding ponds or in early summer when newly developed juveniles are leaving the ponds.

These three species usually divide the habitat. Tiger salamanders are animals of savannas where trees are widely spaced. Spotted salamanders concentrate in forests, while blue spotted salamanders prefer open woodland situations where the tree canopy is less dense. The blue spotted seems to be most abundant in flatwoods.

Salamanders are predators whose major foods include earthworms, insects, and other small invertebrates.

Salamanders vary in the time it takes them to grow to adults. Blue-spotted salamanders may emerge from the breeding pond during the last week in June. Tiger salamanders do not emerge until three or four weeks later.

Salamanders lay their eggs in the water, and the developing young have to stay there. They breathe through gills, so they cannot leave the water until their adult breathing apparatus is ready. This dependence on water can be a problem in dry years. If ponds dry up before the young have matured, the immature animals die. Animals with longer maturation periods—such as the tiger salamander—are particularly vulnerable. Our alterations of the hydrology of our region, alterations that usually lower the water table, are especially hard on amphibians.

FROGS AND TOADS

The toads and frogs of vernal ponds also leave the water after they mature. The western chorus frogs may move out of the woods into wet prairie areas, if any are available. Spring peepers stay in the trees, although they are unlikely to climb very high. Similarly, the gray tree frog (*Hyla chrysoscelis*) generally stays in small trees or low on the trunks of larger trees. Tree frogs have toes equipped with adhesive pads that help them climb and cling to vertical surfaces.

Frogs absorb water through their skins. They can get water simply by sitting in a puddle, but there is now evidence that some species get the water they need from dew clinging to plants. Many of our wooded areas have been heavily infested by invasive trees and shrubs which cast such a heavy shade that groundlayer plants are killed. Such places are less hospitable to amphibians simply because there are no plants for the dew to cling to.

Our one native venomous snake, the massasauga (*Sistrurus catenatus*) is plainly an animal of the savannas, and particularly, the wetter savannas. It may move back and forth from wooded areas to open prairies. Some of this movement may reflect a search for food, but it may also be a search for just the right tempera-

Massasaugas, our only native rattlesnakes, have complex habitat needs. They seem to prefer open savannas where the water table is near the surface. They often occupy crayfish burrows.

ture. Herps cannot regulate their body temperatures as effectively as birds and mammals, so they need to be able to find places to bask in the sun when they are cold and sit in the shade when they are warm. They can use the cooling effects of standing water as a substitute for shade.

Massasaugas eat mice, small birds, frogs, and other snakes. They take over crayfish burrows for shelter, and the bottom of a crayfish burrow is a favored hibernation spot. Crayfish dig down to the water table, so a hibernating massasauga lies in the water, occasionally lifting its head to breathe. Places with clay subsoils that prevent water from draining away are good locations for hibernation.

The raspy songs of Western chorus frogs (above) are a common sound around our forest ponds in spring. Gray tree frogs (right) leave the water after they become adults and ascend into the trees to live.

WETLANDS

In geological terms, the landscape of the Chicago region has existed for just the blink of an eye. Young landscapes like ours, landscapes that have just emerged from under mountains of ice or lakes of water, are very poorly drained.

The elaborate systems of streams and rivers, branching like trees, that develop on older lands, have not yet appeared. Substantial parts of our landscape don't drain at all. Water either sinks into the ground or evaporates. Undrained depressions with no outlets—or with outlets that function only during periods of very high water—are scattered over the entire region.

This young landscape, combined with the many layers of varied deposits left by the glaciers and by post-glacial lakes, produces one of the most diverse collections of wetlands in North America. The pages that follow will describe major features of the most distinctive of these wetland types.

HOW WET ARE THEY?

Some wetlands are submerged year around. Others are wet in spring and early summer and dry by August. In some wetlands, water can be hip-deep. In others, the soil is saturated but little or no water stands above the surface. These differences exert a powerful influence on the vegetation of a wetland. The vegetation, in turn, exerts a major influence on what animals live there.

WHAT IS THE CHEMISTRY?

Soil chemistry plays a particularly important role in two of our wetland types: fens and bogs. Both of these communities depend on conditions created by the glaciers. Fens grow on slopes that are constantly fed by ground water flowing out of sand or gravel deposits. The ground water picks up calcium and magnesium carbonates from the sand and gravel. The highly alkaline water creates conditions that only a select group of calcium-loving plants can tolerate.

Bogs are at the opposite end of the pH scale. Their highly acidic conditions favor the growth of another select group of plants. While fens depend on a constant flow of water, bogs are usually in basins where drainage is either non-existent or extremely limited. Kettleholes in moraines are prime locations for bogs.

Sedge meadows share many species with wet prairies. A string of dry years would allow a sedge meadow to be invaded by prairie species, while a period of unusually wet conditions would allow sedge meadow species to invade the normally drier prairie.

WHERE ARE OUR WETLANDS?

Most of the wetlands in the Midwest have been either drained or filled. In Illinois the loss

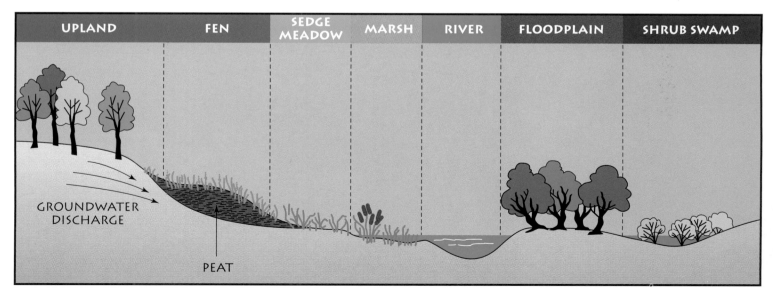

Typical wetland distribution in the Chicago region. Fens occupy hillsides where a constant flow of ground-water keeps them wet. Sedge meadows often grow where soils are saturated but there is little standing water. Marshes need standing water for at least part of the year. Shrub swamps are likely to be in permanently wet ponds. Bogs are usually in isolated depressions.

Early spring in Cowles' Bog at the Indiana Dunes National Lakeshore. The huge leaves of skunk cabbage (Symplocarpus foetidus) grow next to the unfolding fiddle-heads of ferns.

has been greater than 90 percent. In Indiana it is more than 85 percent. Losses in the Chicago Wilderness area have been less drastic than in other parts of these states, but nonetheless most of the wetlands that were here 200 years ago are gone.

Much of the lakeplain where Chicago now stands was wet prairie, sedge meadow, and marsh. Large scale drainage projects have lowered the water table several feet, turning wetland into dry land. The remnant marshes around Lake Calumet are the only surviving wetlands in the city.

For the past century, farmers in our region and throughout the Midwest have been laying drain tile in their fields to make wetlands farmable. Drain tile are placed in deep trenches which are then refilled. The separate pieces of tile are laid end to end, but the joints are not cemented. Water percolating down through the soil enters the tile at the joints and then flows away through the tile.

Elaborate tile systems have been created, with small lines of tile feeding into larger lines which ultimately connect with drainage ditches and rivers.

When conservation agencies buy former farm lands, they either allow these tile systems to decay naturally or deliberately break them up. With the tile gone, former corn fields may return to the hydrology that existed before they were plowed. Frogs and toads may sing again in places that, for a while, were dry land.

LEGAL WETLANDS

The federal Clean Water Act forbids the filling of wetlands. The passage of this law led to the creation of an official legal definition of a wet-land. The U.S. Army Corps of Engineers, which oversees this section of the Clean Water Act, defines wetlands as "areas that are inundated or saturated by surface or ground water at a frequency and duration sufficient to support, and that under normal circumstances do support, a prevalence of vegetation typically adapted for life in saturated soil conditions." "Normal circumstances" means no drain tile, so areas that were wetlands are still wetlands, even if they are temporarily drained dry.

The major concentrations of wetlands in the Chicago Region are on the moraines, along the lower Des Plaines River, and in swales between old beach ridges on the lake plain in Indiana. The percentage figures in the map key refer to the amount of land in each area that is wetland.

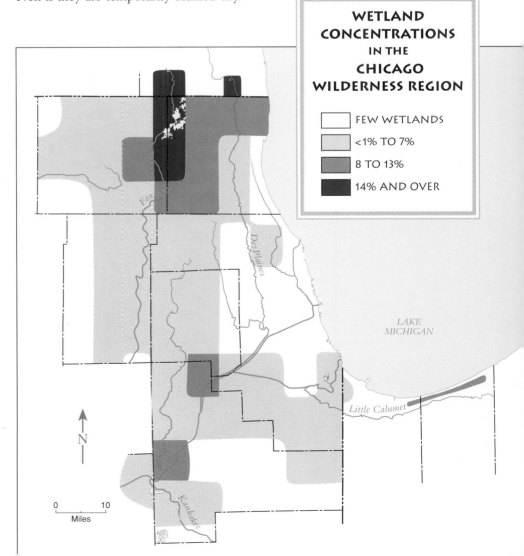

WETLAND CONCENTRATIONS IN THE CHICAGO WILDERNESS REGION

- FEW WETLANDS
- <1% TO 7%
- 8 TO 13%
- 14% AND OVER

LAKE MICHIGAN

Fox

Des Plaines

Little Calumet

Kankakee

N

0   10
Miles

WETLANDS
Marshes and Shrub Swamps

The pink bloom of smartweeds (Polygonum sp.) rise from the waters of a marsh in DuPage County, Illinois.

Cattails

*Our two species of cattails, broad-leaved and narrow-leaved (*Typha latifolia *and* T. angustifolia*), are the two most familiar and easily recognized marsh plants in our region, but the historical evidence we have suggests that they were not very common in the pre-settlement landscape. Indeed, the narrow-leaved cattail may not be native to the region. Siltation and other such disturbances may account for the great increase in cattail populations. Land managers responsible for maintaining healthy, diverse marsh communities worry about the ability of cattails to form dense stands that exclude all other plants.*

Marshes occur in a variety of circumstances in the Chicago Wilderness. Some are found in isolated kettleholes in the moraines. Others are located in the shallow water at the edges of lakes or along the banks of rivers. There are still a few marshes in low places in the Chicago Lake Plain and in the swales between the beach ridges that mark old shorelines of Lake Michigan in northwest Indiana.

Draining and filling have largely eliminated marshes from Illinois outside the Northeast Morainal and Lake Plain divisions and along major rivers. In Indiana, the once vast Kankakee Marshes have been nearly obliterated by drainage projects and the channelizing of the Kankakee River.

Water depth is a major controlling factor of marsh vegetation. In the deep, open waters of lakes and rivers, typical plants are tiny, floating algae that absorb their nutrients from the surrounding water.

In the deepest marsh waters, floating plants, some with submerged leaves, some with floating leaves, replace the algae. However, the more typical marsh plants are emergent species. They are rooted in the bottom and have erect stems that rise above the water. Cattails (*Typha spp.*) are the most familiar of these, but in healthy, diverse marsh communities, cattails are only a part of the plant life.

In late summer, the waters of marshes may turn bright green as duckweed (*Lemma spp.*), the world's smallest flowering plant, seems to cover every square inch of the surface.

Fire played a major role in the ecology of marshes in the past. Of course, the presence of water would tend to prevent fires, but many marshlands are dry in late summer. The productivity of marsh communities provides abundant fuel, producing very hot blazes. The experience of land managers is that periodic fires help maintain the diversity of marsh plant communities.

Shrub swamps grow in shallow ponds. Buttonbush (*Cephalanthus occidentalis*) is the most common dominant in such communities. Other shrubs often present include red-osier dogwood (*Cornus stolonifera*) and various species of willows (*Salix spp.*).

In recent years, a European plant called purple loosestrife (*Lythrum salicaria*) has invaded marshes and other wet areas throughout eastern North America. This aggressive exotic species can completely take over a marsh, driving out native plants and eliminating birds by wiping out the rigid-stemmed plants they use for nest supports. The U.S. Fish & Wildlife Service is currently testing a loosestrife-eating beetle in marshes in the Chicago area to see if this insect can control the loosestrife.

These globular flowers give buttonbushes their common name. The flowers emerge in July and August.

Sedge Meadows

The hummocks created by the sedge called Carex stricta show plainly in early spring. The standing water will be gone before mid-summer and the hummocks will be hidden by new growth.

Sedge meadows are most easily recognized in early spring. Look for low, flat ground flooded with a few inches of water and studded with lumpy tussocks or hummocks. The tussocks reveal the presence of *Carex stricta*, the most common sedge of the sedge meadow.

Sedges belong to the same order of plants as grasses, but they form a separate family within that order. Papyrus, the plant the ancient Egyptians turned into paper, is a sedge, as are bulrushes.

Some 800 species of sedges belong to the genus *Carex*. Almost 150 species of this genus are native to the Chicago region, and several others have been introduced. Most of these are found in various kinds of wet habitats. Some are quite common; others are quite rare. Illinois lists 32 members of the genus as endangered or threatened. This is a reflection of the massive destruction of wetlands that has occurred in the state. Half of these listed species are thought to survive somewhere in the Chicago region. This is a reflection of the survival of greater biodiversity in this region than in the rest of the corn belt.

ORGANIC SOILS

The tussocks of *Carex stricta* are composed of peat formed of the partly decomposed roots and rhizomes (underground stems) of the plant. The soil between the tussocks is also peat. Peat soils are classed as organic soils, meaning they are made almost entirely of the partially decayed remains of once-living plants. Mineral soils, on the other hand, are formed of sand, gravel, silt, clay, and other inorganic materials. Organic soils are common in wetlands where low oxygen levels in the saturated soils prevent the decay of dead plants. If organic soils are composed of peat that has decayed to the point where the individual plant parts that make it up are not identifiable, the soil is called muck.

Several other species of *Carex* are likely to be present in sedge meadows along with a number of species that also occur in other communities—particularly in wet prairies. Canada bluejoint grass (*Calamagrostis canadensis*) is perhaps the most common of these. In late summer, the tall stems of joe pye weed (*Eupatorium maculatum*) are topped by large clusters of purple flowers. Joe pye weed also grows in savannas.

Where the water in a sedge meadow is high in calcium, plants typical of fens can often be found.

Sedge meadows typically flourish where soils remain saturated most of the time, although periods when standing water is present are rare. Fire—which prevents invasion by woody plants—is important to the survival of this community.

Peat will burn if it dries out, so in years when drought strikes, fire could consume the muck soil of the meadow and drastically change conditions. Depending on circumstances such as water levels, marsh vegetation could replace the sedge meadow. If conditions are drier, wet prairie plants could invade.

Some Shared Species of Wet Ground

These three wet communities share many species. The differences among them are more likely to be based on the relative importance of various groups of species rather than on the presence or absence of any particular species.

WETLANDS
Fens

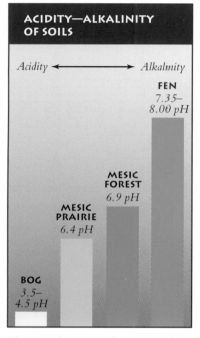

ACIDITY—ALKALINITY OF SOILS

Acidity ⟵ ⟶ *Alkalinity*

FEN
7.35–
8.00 pH

MESIC
FOREST
6.9 pH

MESIC
PRAIRIE
6.4 pH

BOG
3.5–
4.5 pH

The pH scale measures the acidity and alkalinity of organic materials. On this scale, each whole number represents a tenfold change. A fen with a pH of 7.4 is ten times as alkaline as a mesic prairie with a pH of 6.4. Soil pH is an important factor determining the distribution of plants

Fens come in many varieties, but what they all have in common is a continuous source of calcium- and magnesium-rich ground water. In our region, the source of this ground water is in layers of sand or gravel deposited by melt water flowing from a glacier. These sand and gravel aquifers typically sit atop a relatively impermeable layer of glacial drift that prevents water from sinking farther below the surface.

Since it can't go down, the water flows sideways until it emerges on a slope. Along the way, the water has picked up the minerals that give fens their unique chemistry. The flow river was a torrent carrying a flood of meltwater from the wasting glacier. Others are similarly situated in glacial deposits where erosion has exposed gravel aquifers on hillsides.

In some places, the flowing ground water carries such a heavy load of minerals that some of them precipitate out and form a porous rock called tufa. Sometimes, marl, a loose, crumbly material formed of calcium and other minerals, collects. Fen soils are formed of peat.

Places with high mineral concentrations and heavy flows may be separated out as spring runs or marl flats. Calcareous seeps are areas

White lady slippers (Cypripedium candidum) are among the beautiful orchids that show an affinity for the alkaline, peaty soils of fens.

from the aquifer may be sufficient to keep the water liquid through the winter.

Terrain, the amount of flow, and the amounts of minerals in the water all affect the precise nature of the fen community. In small amounts, calcium is an important plant nutrient. At high concentrations, it creates caustic conditions that place strong limitations on plant life. Only species adapted to these unusual conditions can live in fens.

Many of our fens are along the Fox River on the slopes of morainal hills, kames, and gravel terraces left from the time when the with high flow but with more organic matter and nutrients in their soils than occur in spring runs. Graminoid fens occur where flow is reduced and still more nutrients and organic matter are in the soil. Graminoid fens share many plants with the prairies. Such dominant prairie grasses as big and little bluestem (*Andropogon spp.*) and Indian grass (*Sorghastrum nutans*) can be found growing along with calcium-loving species like grass-of-parnassus (*Parnassia glauca*) and Ohio goldenrod (*Solidago ohiensis*). Sedges are also common.

Graminoid fens depend on periodic fire. If fire cannot reach them, shrubs and trees invade.

Bogs

Open water, sedge mats, and bog forest appear in this picture of Volo Bog in Lake (IL) and McHenry Counties. The sundew (left) uses sticky filaments to capture insects.

Bogs are remnants of a time when the Chicago Wilderness region was covered with vegetation like that of present-day Upper Michigan. In early post-glacial time, a spruce-fir forest dominated this region. As oak-woods and prairies replaced this boreal forest on the uplands, bogs hung on in small glacial depressions where drainage was limited or totally absent.

Bogs are striking examples of the ability of plants to change their environment. They can, over time, fill a pond or small lake with peat that forms a substrate firm enough to support trees.

Bog waters are cold, extremely acid, and very low in oxygen. Mineral nutrients are locked up in the peat and therefore unavailable to plants. These conditions place severe limits on plant life. A group of species has adapted to these conditions. These bog plants dominate this extreme environment and are unlikely to be found anywhere else.

Bog development is likely to begin with the formation of a floating mat of plants. Sedges are a major element in this mat as are mosses, particularly Sphagnum moss.

As this mat thickens, it becomes firm enough to allow shrubs to root in it. Bog birch (*Betula pumila*) may begin to grow, along with leatherleaf (*Chamaedaphne calyculata*) and other species of heaths, among them, cranberries (*Vaccinium macrocarpon*). In time, trees may invade, particularly tamarack (*Larix laricina*), a deciduous conifer whose needles turn a rich gold before dropping in the fall.

In our region, the final stage in this process is considered to be a tall-shrub bog dominated by winterberry (*Ilex verticillata*) and poison sumac (*Rhus vernix*). The exotic shrub glossy buckthorn (*Rhamnus frangula*) has invaded this community in recent years.

The stages in bog development can often be seen as a series of concentric circles in existing bogs. The outermost circle is a narrow moat of open water next to the shore of the lake or pond. Inside that is a sedge mat, then a low shrub bog, a forested bog, and a tall-shrub bog. A small pond of open water may remain at the center of this sequence.

In the nutrient-poor environment of the bog, some plants have developed the ability to capture insects to provide themselves with nitrogen and other essential elements. The sundews (*Drosera spp.*) snare their prey on sticky filaments. The pitcher plants (*Sarracenia spp.*) trap insects in cups baited with sugar water.

Bogs are known for the beauty of their flowers. The heath shrubs produce bell-like blooms and miniature versions of azaleas. A number of orchids—like the stemless lady slipper (*Cypripedium acaule*)—are bog specialists. Others, like the grass pink (*Calopogon tuberosus*) are often found there.

The grass pink (Calopogon tuberosus) decorates summer bogs with its flowers. This species can also be found at the other end of the pH scale in fens.

WETLANDS
Insects

The green darner (Anax junius) hawks for mosquitoes above the wetlands of Chicago Wilderness.

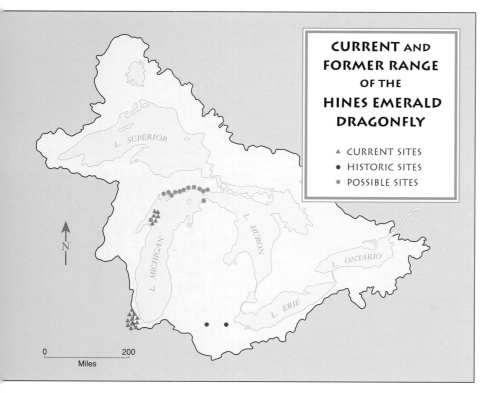

CURRENT AND FORMER RANGE OF THE HINES EMERALD DRAGONFLY

▲ CURRENT SITES
● HISTORIC SITES
● POSSIBLE SITES

L. SUPERIOR
L. MICHIGAN
L. HURON
L. ONTARIO
L. ERIE

N

0   200
Miles

Dragonflies are among the most familiar sights at summer marshes. These ancient insects—their ancestry goes back to the coal forests—are predators that win the affection of humans by eating mosquitoes. Their larvae live in water where they prey on small aquatic creatures.

At a few special places in Chicago Wilderness, wet places along the lower Des Plaines River where a torrent of meltwater scraped away the glacial debris and exposed the 400 million year old bedrock, a bright green dragonfly called the Hines emerald (*Somatochlora hinena*) hunts insects over marshes, sedge meadows, and forest edges. The Hines emerald is known from a few sites in Cook and Will Counties; it is known from a few sites in Wisconsin's Door County where this same dolomite bedrock is exposed. Historical records exist from northern Ohio on the same bedrock.

The Chicago Region is at the center of efforts to protect this rare and endangered insect.

Birds

Wetlands are rich in bird life. Dabbling ducks like the blue-winged teal (*Anas discors*) sit on the surface scooping up duckweed, sedge seeds, and snails. Pied-billed grebes (*Podilymbus podiceps*) use their control of their own buoyancy to sink like submerging submarines until only their heads remain above the surface, then dive in search of small fish, crayfish, and tadpoles.

Soras slip among the reeds searching out snails, insects, and smartweed seeds. The marsh wren (*Cistothorus palustris*) sings its rattling song from the cattails and yellow-headed blackbirds (*Xanthocephalus xanthocephalus*) sing a song that sounds like somebody dropping a handful of nails in a coffee grinder.

Great blue herons stand motionless in shallow water waiting for a fish to get careless and reveal its position while black terns (*Chlidonias niger*) swoop through the air picking off flying insects.

Lists of endangered and threatened birds are depressingly heavy on wetland species. Three of the birds mentioned above are on the endangered list in Illinois. The Chicago region is a refuge for these

birds simply because so many wetlands still survive here.

Perhaps our most vulnerable birds are the big colonial nesters. The loss of a single nesting location can leave dozens—in some cases hundreds—of potential nesting pairs without a home. Five species of these colonial nesters live in the Chicago Wilderness, although the cattle egret lives at only one site, Will County's Lake Renwick. Cattle egrets

A common moorhen (Gallinula chloropus) helps her chicks learn to recognize food. A threatened species in Illinois, the moorhen nests in several locations in our region. These birds were photographed at Chicago's Lake Calumet.

are African birds that managed to get to North America on their own. They nest in wetlands, but they usually feed in pastures.

The double-crested cormorant is actually more of a river and lake bird than a wetland bird. This diving bird may go down 25 feet or more after fish. It would find little to interest it in seasonal ponds.

The colonial herons--the great blue, the great egret, and the black-crowned night heron- fish the shallow waters. Their usual hunting strategy is to stand very still and wait for something to move. They usually grab things in their bills, although the great blue may use its bill as a spear for capturing larger fish.

Great blue herons and great egrets are off and flying by dawn, looking for ponds and marshes that are likely hunting areas. Black crowned night herons, as their name suggests, do more of their work after dark. They leave their nesting grounds at dusk. The night herons usually nest in trees, but at the Big Marsh near Lake Calumet, they have adapted to nesting on the ground amid rushes.

Large numbers of big birds need large areas for hunting. These birds may travel 10 to 15 miles in search of food. It takes lots of small wetlands to support the animals living in one rookery in one big wetland.

The most familiar wetland bird is the red-winged blackbird (*Agelaius phoeniceus*), a wetland species that has invaded uplands in recent years. Red-wings seem to do well even where cattails have completely covered all the water in a wetland. Yellow-headed blackbirds appear to need some open water.

Lake Renwick is an old gravel quarry in Will County that is our largest rookery. All five of our colonial nesting waterbirds nest on the islands in this lake.

Colonial nesters of the Chicago region include double-crested cormorants (Phalacrocorax auritus), great blue herons (Ardea herodias), great egrets (Casmerodius albus), black-crowned night herons (Nycticorax nycticorax), and cattle egrets (Bubulcus ibis). Cattle egrets nest only at Lake Renwick in Will county. Numbers on rookery sites show number of colonial species nesting at the location.

Soras (Porzana carolina) slip between the stems of emergent vegetation in search of insects, snails, and seeds. Smart-weed seeds are a favorite food.

WETLANDS
Mammals

The river otter was once common in our region, but has been extirpated. As water quality improves in our rivers, the reintroduction of this species is a possibility.

Mink tracks

The skins of beavers were the first products of the Midwest to enter the world market. Native Americans controlled this end of the trade in the early days, but late in the 1600s, the French arrived. Later, British and American traders took over the business. The hides of other animals were traded too, but beavers (*Castor canadensis*) made up the bulk of the commerce. Their skins were turned into hats in Europe.

The trapping of beavers was a huge business, so big that it eventually killed all the beavers. Historical accounts say that by about 1850, beavers were completely gone not only from the Chicago Region but from the rest of Illinois and Indiana as well.

They are now found in suitable habitat throughout the Chicago region. The return of the beaver was accomplished with a certain amount of stocking, but mainly, the beavers made it back on their own. They were helped by the extensive network of drainage ditches dug to keep the water out of croplands across Illinois.

Beavers not only live in wetlands, they make wetlands. Their dams turn sections of streams into ponds. The dams deepen the water providing room for underwater entrances to beaver lodges. Along larger rivers where banks are suitable the beavers live in burrows with underwater entrances.

Muskrats (*Ondatra zibethicus*) are the most visible of marsh mammals. They are frequently seen swimming, especially near dawn and dusk. Their houses are low domes—much smaller than beaver lodges—roofed with mud and marsh plants. Birds as diverse as Canada geese (*Branta canadensis*) and black terns nest on top of muskrat houses.

Muskrats are prolific animals. When populations are at peak levels, their appetites can significantly reduce cattail stands.

Mink (*Mustela vison*) eat muskrats and virtually anything else they can overpower. They sometimes take over muskrat houses after eating the inhabitants. They are active mainly at night, but sometimes continue hunting into the morning when early visitors might catch sight of one.

River otters (*Lutra canadensis*) were once part of the Chicago Wilderness. They have been extirpated from much of their former range in the Midwest. Today, they are occasionally seen along the Mississippi and in extreme southern Illinois.

Occasional sightings, including some from McHenry, Kane, and DuPage County in recent years, were probably wandering individuals looking for a home. With better water quality and some limits on development along rivers, they might find one.

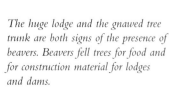

The huge lodge and the gnawed tree trunk are both signs of the presence of beavers. Beavers fell trees for food and for construction material for lodges and dams.

Herps

A female Blanding's turtle (*Emydoidea blandingii*) was captured at Spring Bluff Preserve, a Lake County (IL) forest preserve on Lake Michigan immediately south of the Wisconsin Border. She was equipped with a radio tracking device and released. She began traveling north, crossing the state line into the Chiwaukee Prairie, a preserve managed by The Nature Conservancy of Wisconsin. There she took up residence at a pond. She had traveled a total of 765 meters, about half a mile.

RANGE OF BLANDING'S TURTLE IN ILLINOIS

In her wandering, she crossed land held by a county preserve system and a private conservation organization. In Illinois, she was a member of a species on a "watch list." The watch list is reserved for animals and plants whose future is a matter of concern but who are not considered in sufficient peril to make the endangered or threatened list. However, when she crossed the state line, this turtle became a member of a threatened species, since that is the status of Blanding's turtle in Wisconsin.

The travels of this turtle point up the importance of cooperation among conservation agencies and states. They also emphasize the importance of preserving wetlands—even small wetlands. Many animals visit wetlands too small to support permanent populations. Some wetlands can support small populations that may die out from time to time. These populations must be replenished by migrants from other areas, and that recolonization cannot happen if great distances or other obstacles prevent it.

Adult Blanding's turtles prefer shallow ponds with at least some open water. They do not live where dense stands of cattails dominate the wetland. Young animals of this species have been observed in several different kinds of wetlands. They have been known to live in burrows dug into the hummocks created by *Carex stricta* in sedge meadows.

Many wetland herps are confined to areas with permanent water. Snapping turtles (*Chelydra serpentina*) belong to this group as do bullfrogs (*Rana catesbeiana*).

Kirtland's snake (*Clonophis kirtlandii*) is a species that can be defined as an animal of wet prairies, wet savannas, or wetlands. Like the massasauga, it uses crayfish burrows, and it spends much time in them. Earthworms are a major food source and they may be captured underground.

*Blanding's turtle (*Emydoidea blandingii*) (above left) is a once-common wetland species that has been eliminated in most of its historic range by habitat loss. The map shows the historic range in color. The triangles indicate locations of recent sightings of the species. Baby snapping turtles (above) will look for permanent bodies of water to provide them with a home.*

STILL WATERS
Lakes and Ponds

The longear sunfish (Lepomis megalotis) brightens the waters of both lakes and rivers in this region.

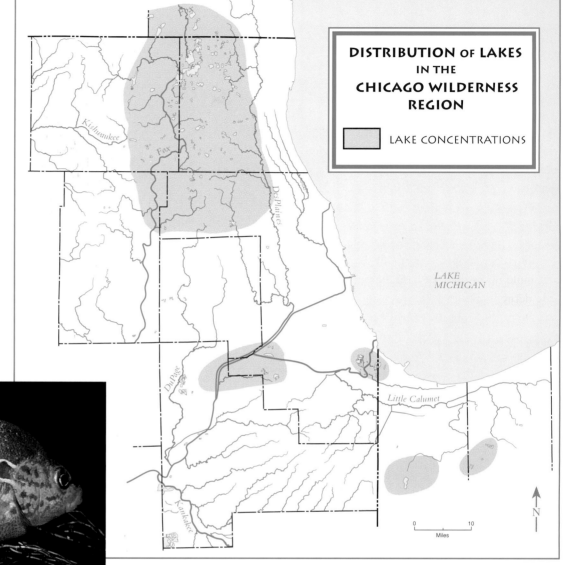

DISTRIBUTION OF LAKES
IN THE
CHICAGO WILDERNESS
REGION

LAKE CONCENTRATIONS

LAKE MICHIGAN

Lakes in our region are concentrated on the moraines and in low spots on the Chicago Lake Plain. Draining and filling have eliminated all but a few of the lake-plain lakes.

Lakes are one of the signs of the youth of our landscape. In areas to the south and west, where the glaciers departed less recently, the various depressions left by the ice have drained away or been filled by erosion from the surrounding uplands.

Glacial lakes are common to the north in Wisconsin and Michigan, but in the states of Illinois and Indiana, they are almost entirely confined to the small portion of each state that lies on the Valparaiso Moraine or on the younger lands between the moraine and Lake Michigan.

Lakes are permanently, not just seasonally, wet. They are too deep for rooted plants to grow except in shallow, near-shore areas. The distinction between a lake and a pond is a matter of size. Lakes are bodies of water large enough to have at least one wind-swept beach. When winds are high, they blow across the water and create waves large enough to wash away any plants attempting to colonize the beach.

Our inland lakes are generally of moderate depth. One, in Lake County (IL), reaches a depth of 50 feet and has been named Deep Lake. Thirty to 35 feet is more usual.

Lakes and ponds can be divided into categories based on abundance of nutrients and how these nutrients are cycled through them. Oligotrophic lakes contain limited nutrients and maintain an approximate balance between production of organic material by photosynthesis and decomposition. The process of decay releases nutrients back to the water. The open waters of Lake Michigan are oligotrophic.

In eutrophic lakes and ponds (the name means "well fed"), nutrients are abundant and more are taken up during production than are released by decay. Such lakes usually receive a continuing supply of nutrients through run-off from surrounding lands. Sediments rich in organic matter build up on the bottom, and the lake gradually fills. In the deeper waters, the bacteria of decay may absorb all the available oxygen, creating stagnant conditions where few animals can live. Stagnation is most frequent during late summer when the supply of oxygen brought to the deep waters by the spring overturn—see graphic on this page—has been exhausted. Many inland lakes are usually eutrophic.

In dystrophic lakes, production and reduction are wildly out of balance. Bogs are good examples of dystrophic waters. Thick layers of peat build up in the lake basin because very little decay is taking place.

One of the common effects of settlement has been a large increase in the amounts of nutrients flowing into our lakes and ponds. These come from fertilizers, from sewage treatment plants, or leaking septic systems. They push lakes in the direction of dystrophy by greatly increasing the amount of production. Algae blooms fertilized by these nutrients can also be foul smelling.

Lakes are ecologically complex communities with several distinctive kinds of organisms living in them. On the bottom are mussels, tube worms, and fresh water sponges.

Swimming organisms include crustaceans and other invertebrates as well as fish. Healthy lake communities have animals at different trophic—that is, feeding—levels, from herbivores to top carnivores. Fish-eating birds such as cormorants and terns enter the picture as predators.

Several endangered and threatened species live in the lakes of the Chicago region, most of them in the lakes of the Fox River watershed. They include several small fish belonging to the genus *Notropis* that carry the common name "shiners." Shiners are seldom more than six inches long and often much smaller. They feed on insects and small crustaceans.

The plight of the shiners is usually a product of environmental changes in their home lakes. The Illinois Endangered Species Board has recommended that glacial lakes be protected from further development and from pollution and herbicides, that introduction of sport fish be prohibited, and that native submerged and emergent vegetation be protected and enhanced.

*The cup-like leaves and yellow flowers of American lotus (*Nelumbo lutea*) cover the shallow water in Nippersink Lake in Lake County, IL.*

LAKE STRATIFICATION AND TURNOVER

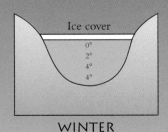

WINTER

Heating and cooling separate lake waters into layers. In winter the cold air chills water near the surface. The warmest water is in the depths.

SPRING
(turnover)

Spring sunshine heats the surface layers until all the water is the same temperature. Mixing by wind and currents brings oxygen-rich water to the depths.

SUMMER
(layering)

In summer, the warm water is at the surface. A sharply defined *thermocline* divides the warm surface water from the deep cold water.

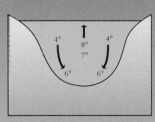

FALL
(turnover)

Fall cooling produces uniform temperatures again and another turnover. The turnovers are the principal sources of oxygen in the deep waters of lakes.

MOVING WATERS
Streams and Rivers

The North Branch of the Chicago River is a peaceful stream on a sunny summer day. The creation of preserves along the rivers is helping return life to the waters.

The rivers of the Chicago region have been subjected to the same kinds of humiliations as other rivers in major industrial, population, and agricultural centers. They have been used at times as open sewers. They have been dumping grounds for industrial wastes and been muddied with run-off from plowed fields. The Chicago in Illinois and the Grand Calumet in Indiana got the worst of this treatment, although no river escaped without some damage.

Over the last 25 years, since the passage of the Clean Water Act and other legislation, conditions have improved somewhat. Fish that have not been seen in a century have returned to the Chicago; herons can be seen in the marshes along the Grand Cal. According to the Biological Stream Characterization of the Illinois Department of Natural Resources, some Chicago region streams qualify as "Unique Aquatic Resources," Class A, or "Highly Valued Aquatic Resources," Class B. The lower Kankakee as it flows through Will County is a river whose biodiversity makes it of global significance.

The use of rivers by living things is largely controlled by physical and chemical factors. Physical factors include the size of the river and the amount of water flowing through it, the consistency of the flow, the speed of the current, and the nature of the bottom. Chemical factors in our region are mostly about the extent of pollution.

Biologists have divided the rivers of the Chicago region into four size categories. The smallest of these is the headwater stream, a tiny creek that may flow only intermittently. Headwater streams have few species of fish, and most of those are shiners and other minnows.

Low order streams are small- to medium-sized creeks whose bottoms have been shaped by the water to produce riffles and pools, alternating sections of fast shallow water and slow deep water. Life in these streams often sorts itself into ripple and pool species. The creek heelsplitter (*Lasmigona compressa*), an endangered mussel known in recent years from the Kishwaukeee and tributaries of the Kankakee, is a quiet water species. Among fish, the threatened river redhorse (*Moxostoma carinatum*) is a riffle species, while the threatened Iowa darter (*Etheostoma exile*) is a fish of quiet pools.

Many miles of streams in the Chicago region have been channelized, that is, dredged into straight, steep-sided ditches of uniform depth. Channelized streams have neither riffles nor pools. Dams on our rivers, by preventng upstream movement, also contribute to the decline in biodiversity.

Mid-order streams are our most complex river habitat. Water flows through both deep and shallow pools. In the riffles, smallmouth bass (*Micropterus dolomieui*) are top predators, while largemouth bass (*Micropterus salmoides*) live in the pools. Floodplains begin to develop along streams of this size.

Our largest rivers have broad floodplains. Floodplains are low lands adjoining the river channel that are regularly flooded during periods—such as early spring—of heavy flow. The flooding exerts a heavy influence on vegetation along the banks.

Our presence in the watersheds has dramatically changed the pattern of flow in our rivers. If the surrounding watershed is largely natural land, heavy rains or snow melt tend to be absorbed by the soil and released gradually. We have turned much of our watersheds into impervious surfaces—pavement and roofs. Water is carried rapidly to the river by storm sewers and produces frequent flooding.

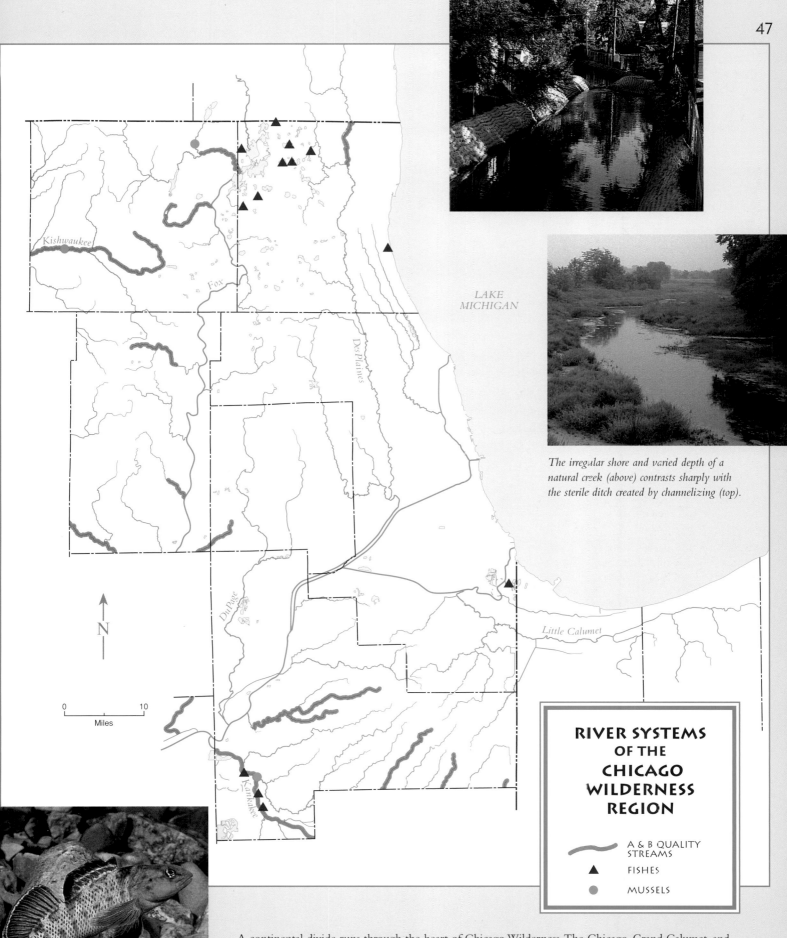

The irregular shore and varied depth of a
natural creek (above) contrasts sharply with
the sterile ditch created by channelizing (top).

*LAKE
MICHIGAN*

Kishwaukee

Fox

DesPlaines

DuPage

N

0   10
  Miles

Little Calumet

Kankakee

**RIVER SYSTEMS
OF THE
CHICAGO
WILDERNESS
REGION**

A & B QUALITY
STREAMS

▲ FISHES

● MUSSELS

Rainbow darter (Etheostoma caeruleum) is one
of the endangered species that still lives in our
river systems.

A continental divide runs through the heart of Chicago Wilderness. The Chicago, Grand Calumet, and
Little Calumet Rivers flow into Lake Michigan. The Des Plaines and Kankakee Rivers join to create
the Illinois River which flows to the Mississippi. The Fox also joins the Illinois. The Kishwaukee flows
to the Mississippi via the Rock River. A century ago, the flow of the Chicago was reversed. It now
flows through the Sanitary and Ship Canal into the Des Plaines and the Illinois. Rare and endangered
fish and mussels still live in the best of our rivers.

THE DUNES

Fowler's toad (Bufo woodhousii fowleri) is a duneland specialist not found elsewhere in our region.

Henry Chandler Cowles

The University of Chicago's Professor Cowles was one of the founders of the science of ecology. His studies of plant life at the Indiana Dunes developed the idea of ecological succession and connected the history of the land to the life it supports.

Henry Chandler Cowles is said to have developed his interest in the Indiana Dunes after passing through the area on a train during his first trip to Chicago. The landscape that Cowles glimpsed is one of the most diverse in North America. Open dunes, marshes, prairies, upland forests and swamps, oak savannas, and relict populations of jack pines all grow within a few miles of the Lake Michigan shore. Botanical surveys tell us that more species of plants grow in the Indiana Dunes National Lakeshore than in Great Smoky Mountains National Park.

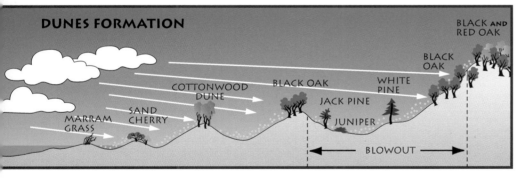

DUNES FORMATION

BLACK **AND** RED OAK

BLACK OAK

BLACK OAK   WHITE PINE

JACK PINE

COTTONWOOD DUNE

JUNIPER

SAND CHERRY

MARRAM GRASS

BLOWOUT

The beach at the Indiana Dunes is a windswept desert where only a few hardy annuals can live. South from the beach, the land is progressively older and more extensively modified by the plant communities that cover it. The vegetation separates into narrow bands of very different communities. These differences help give the dunes their great biodiversity.

The basis of this diversity is the shape of the land. As part of the lake plain, the dunes show the history of the various stages and levels of Lake Michigan. Long beach ridges parallel the present shoreline. Between them are low swales now occupied by lakes, marshes, and other wetlands.

The most spectacular sights are the dunes themselves, mountains of sand rising nearly a hundred feet above the swales. These dunes sit atop glacial drift. They have formed through the millenia from sand blown by the prevailing westerly winds, sand taken from the endless supply carried by near-shore currents in Lake Michigan.

Illinois has its dune lands too. At Illinois Beach State Park marram grass (*Ammophila brevigulata*) grows on low foredunes immediately behind the beach, and sand savannas dominated by black oak (*Quercus velutina*) are a major community type. But there are no high dunes at Illinois Beach, because the prevailing winds blow toward the lake. Illinois Beach is also a much younger landscape. It was formed in the past 3,000 years, while parts of the dunelands of Indiana go back to the earliest periods of Lake Michigan's development.

The story that Cowles pieced together from his researches at the Indiana Dunes was of changes wrought largely by plants on the landscape in which they grew. Adding organic matter to the soil, changing the microclimate by casting shade or shielding land from the winds, the marram grass of the foredunes would eventually create conditions that would favor the growth of other plants, and these plants would replace the marram grass.

The process was called ecological succession, and it became a major concept in the then young science of ecology. Succession was thought to lead ultimately to a natural community called the regional climax, a single, stable, long-lived community that would cover the entire landscape.

Cowles made ecological change intelligible, although today, we think of the idea of a climax community as too directional. No landscape ever reaches the regional climax. Instead, a variety of forces act to maintain diversity. The winter storm that blows down trees and opens new opportunities for marram grass is not a setback on the road to the regional climax but a predictably recurring event that sustains biodiversity.

LAKE MICHIGAN

The Great Lakes are among the wonders of the world. The five inland seas hold one-sixth of the world's surface fresh water. Lake Michigan is the third largest of the lakes, with a surface area of 22,300 square miles.

The lake has played a major role in the history of the Chicago region. It has been a highway for traders, travelers, and immigrants.

The natural riches of the lake were major resources. Commercial fishing in the lake was a big business and, for much of its history, it was totally unregulated. Over-fishing pushed some species to the brink of extinction. By the late 1930s, lake trout (*Salvelinus namaycush*) numbers had been seriously reduced. The arrival of sea lampreys (*Petromyzon marinus*) in the forties finished off the species. Lampreys, an Atlantic species that entered the Upper Great Lakes via the Welland Canal, are parasites on fish, and heavy infestations can be lethal. By the time another kind of newcomer, the alewife (*Alosa pseudoharengus*), arrived, the lake had no top predator to help control the numbers of this very prolific exotic species. Alewife populations boomed and then crashed in massive die-offs that littered beaches in the late sixties.

In the early seventies, various species of salmon, including the coho (*Oncorhynchus kisutch*), were introduced to control the alewives. They succeeded at that and, as a sort of side effect, created a multi-billion dollar sport fishing industry.

Meanwhile, lake trout stocking continued, but the species showed few signs of being able to reproduce naturally. New exotic species arrived, the most troublesome being the zebra mussel (*Dreissena polymorpha*), a mollusc that now infests practically every suitable bit of lake bottom. Traditionally abundant species such as the yellow perch (*Perca flavescens*) have been declining alarmingly.

Not long ago, it was the water quality of Lake Michigan that was declining. A concerted international effort has produced major improvements—although problems with persistent toxic chemicals remain. However, the biological quality of the lake is very much in question. Aquatic biologists have the heavy task of trying to maintain a system in the face of the constant arrival of new exotic species and the loss of coastal habitat.

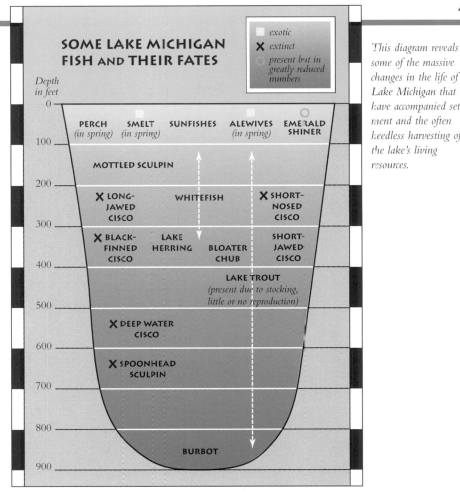

SOME LAKE MICHIGAN FISH AND THEIR FATES

□ exotic
✕ extinct
○ present but in greatly reduced numbers

Depth in feet

PERCH (in spring)	SMELT (in spring)	SUNFISHES	ALEWIVES (in spring)	EMERALD SHINER
MOTTLED SCULPIN				
✕ LONG-JAWED CISCO		WHITEFISH		✕ SHORT-NOSED CISCO
✕ BLACK-FINNED CISCO		LAKE HERRING	BLOATER CHUB	SHORT-JAWED CISCO
		LAKE TROUT (present due to stocking, little or no reproduction)		
✕ DEEP WATER CISCO				
✕ SPOONHEAD SCULPIN				
		BURBOT		

This diagram reveals some of the massive changes in the life of Lake Michigan that have accompanied settlement and the often heedless harvesting of the lake's living resources.

Zebra mussels (inset) are the latest exotic species to upset the ecological balance of the Great Lakes. These tiny molluscs now occupy practically every square inch of suitable habitat in Lake Michigan.

PEOPLE ON THE LAND

Native Americans

People have been living in the Chicago region for thousands of years. It is likely that hunters followed the big animals such as mastodons north as the glaciers receded. In those times, human populations were small—as they were throughout the world—and hunting and gathering were the sole means of subsistence.

By 2,000 years ago, people in the Midwest were living in settled communities based upon a combination of agriculture and the harvest of natural foods such as fish, shellfish, and game. These communities developed into substantial societies capable of building such impressive works as the mounds at Cahokia, Illinois, and other Midwestern sites.

This Midwestern civilization was centered along the major rivers: the Illinois, Mississippi, and Ohio.

The arrival of Europeans in North America was catastrophic for native societies. Diseases such as smallpox and measles destroyed whole communities. Tribes displaced by the new colonists pushed west and came into conflict with people already there.

The Illini, a confederation of peoples that had greeted the first French explorers in the late 1600s, had practically ceased to exist by 1800. The Potawatomi, recent arrivals from the eastern shore of Lake Michigan, had occupied the Chicago region by the time the city was founded in the 1830s.

Native populations were small. Only a few thousand people lived in the Chicago region. Their way of life and their habitations followed the seasons. Spring and summer were spent in towns living in wooden houses. Fields near the towns were planted in corn, beans, and squash.

After the harvest, most people moved away from the towns. Often only a few elderly people remained there through the winter. The rest of the population moved into winter hunting camps. The camps were occupied by family groups.

The coming of spring was signaled by the gathering of the people at groves of black and sugar maple. There,

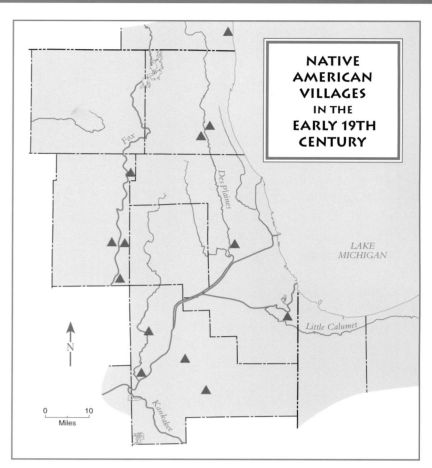

The permanent villages of Native Americans in this region were mainly along the rivers. People made seasonal use of the lake plain—where the present city of Chicago is located—but they didn't live on that wet, wind-swept land.

they collected the rising sap and boiled it down into maple sugar, which they used as a condiment much as we use salt.

The Potawatomi towns were mainly along the rivers. There they had reliable water supplies and firewood. The prairies were places they used seasonally for hunting and gathering. They had no reason to establish permanent towns there.

The major crops of the Potawatomi were of tropical origin and did not escape into the wild. Extensive trade networks existed throughout North America, but the goods traded were mainly portable commodities and luxury goods. The sort of bulk shipments that led to the accidental importation of large numbers of plants from Europe were not part of Native American commerce.

This way of life began to change after the fur trade became important as men turned more of their time and attention to trapping and hunting beaver and other fur-bearers. Iron pots and steel axes, acquired in exchange for furs, replaced pottery and stone tools. In the first 150 years of European presence, the newcomers and natives adapted to each other. It was only after the Americans began to pour in that natives were forced to move west.

The largest effect of Native Americans on the landscape came from their use of fire as a land management tool. The earliest account of burning in North America

Ruth Duncan and her daughter, members of the Lenape tribe, demonstrate the proper technique for building a wigwam at a maple sugar festival at the Indiana Dunes National Lakeshore.

dates from 1528 when Cabeza de Vaca saw people in Texas setting fires. In the seventeenth century, French traders planned journeys west from the Mississippi to miss the fall fire season. Accounts of fires in Illinois, Indiana, and southern Wisconsin are numerous.

Fires gave a competitive edge to the natural communities best adapted to them. They created the varied landscape of prairie, savanna, woodland and forest that greeted settlers in the early 19th century. Fire is a natural process in many ecosystems, and many natural communities are adapted to regular blazes. The native peoples made use of this process to serve their own needs, but their actions protected and often increased the biodiversity of the region.

Settlement

Jean Baptiste Point du Sable, a man of mixed African and French ancestry, established the first trading post at the mouth of the Chicago River when this region was still under British control.

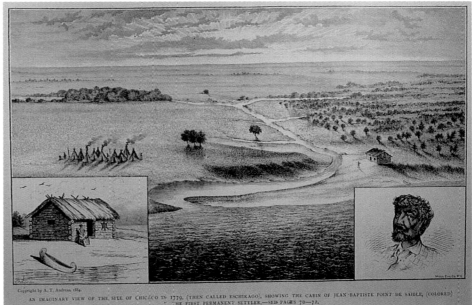

AN IMAGINARY VIEW OF THE SITE OF CHICAGO IN 1779, (THEN CALLED ESCHIKAGO), SHOWING THE CABIN OF JEAN-BAPTISTE POINT DE SAIBLE, (COLORED) THE FIRST PERMANENT SETTLER.—SEE PAGES 70–72.

Jean Baptiste Point du Sable set up his trading post at the mouth of the Chicago River just as Americans along the Atlantic coast were rebelling against the colonial government of England and setting up their new republic. Du Sable—of mixed French and African ancestry—was one of many traders in the Midwest who bought furs from the native people and paid for them with iron pots, steel axes, woolen blankets, and a variety of other commodities that had already, by the 1770s, profoundly changed the lives of Native Americans.

The society of the Midwest at the time was a blend of native peoples and small numbers of traders from elsewhere. Intermarriage was common and close ties developed across cultural barriers. Except for the devastating attack on the beaver, changes in the human landscape had little effect on the natural landscape.

All that changed suddenly and profoundly after the United States gained control of the lands that are now in the Chicago region after the War of 1812. Settlers began to pour in. The government land office sent out teams of surveyors to mark off the land so it could be sold to settlers. The survey reports are now one of our important sources of information about the native vegetation of this region.

Chicago was meant to be a city from the beginning. Farmers who took up land at the edges of town were quickly overrun by development. By 1870, 350,000 people lived in Cook County, and the city's population would top one million before the end of the century.

In the rest of the region, settlement followed a more typical pattern, as farmers settled the land and market towns sprang up to serve them. In northwest Indiana, settlement was concentrated in the better lands on the moraine. The lake plain with its marshes and dunes had little attraction for farmers.

Prairie soils proved to be extraordinarily fertile, and unplowed prairies became pastures. The eating habits of cows and horses proved to be different than those of bison and elk, and some common prairie wildflowers began to disappear. Suppression of fire and the influx of exotic species that came with the settlers also made life difficult for many of the prairie natives.

Land that had been brushy prairie during times when fires were a regular occurrence quickly became oak woods after settlement. Meanwhile,

burban development, but this was confined to towns along the rail lines and was, for the most part, something that only the well-to-do could enjoy.

Settlement patterns began to change dramatically after World War II. Federal mortgage guarantees strongly favored new housing, encouraging the development of new neighborhoods and whole new towns. The building of the Interstate highway system in the fifties and early sixties made long-distance commuting practical, not just between the city center and outlying areas but from any point in the metropolis to any other point.

Suburban areas have grown explosively in the past 50 years. Chicago, meanwhile, hit its population peak in the fifties and has been losing people ever since.

Business and industry moved to the suburbs too. Corporate headquarters that occupied a few floors of a high-rise in the Loop became 40-acre corporate campuses in the suburbs. The region grew like a fairy ring mushroom,

PATENT   CARY
PLOUGH.

JOHN DEERE respectfully informs his friends and customers, the agricultural community, of this and the adjoining counties, and dealers in Ploughs, that he is now prepared to fill orders for the same on presentation.

The mould board of this well, and so favorably known PLOUGH, is made of wrought iron, and the share of steel, 5-16th of an inch thick, which carries a fine sharp edge.   The whole face of the mould board and share is ground smooth, so that it scours perfectly bright in any soil, and will not choke in the foulest of ground.   It will do more work in a day, and do it much better and with much less labor, to both team and holder, than the ordinary ploughs that do not scour, and in consequence of the ground being better prepared the agriculturalist obtains a much heavier crop.

☞The price of Ploughs, in conse-quence of hard times, will be reduced from last year's prices.
Grand Detour, Feb. 3, 1843.   2tf

An Illinois blacksmith named John Deere invented the steel moldboard plow that allowed farmers to till the heavy soils of the prairie.

the places that had been forested were cut over, and drainage projects were eating away at wetlands.

During the first century of settlement, human populations tended to be concentrated. In Chicago and in the smaller industrial towns like Joliet, Elgin, and Gary, most workers lived near their jobs, either walking to work or commuting by street car or other public transit. The coming of railroads led to some sur-

endlessly expanding at the margins while the center died.

Chicago lost more than 100,000 jobs in manufacturing in less than 30 years. In northwest Indiana, the older industrial areas in Gary, Hammond, and East Chicago saw major population declines while towns to the south were booming.

The shift from high density housing and business to low density suburbs has put a heavy demand on land. For decades, the amount of developed land has been increasing at a rate several times larger than the population. Both farm land and natural land are rapidly being converted to homes and businesses.

Meanwhile, evidence has begun to collect that urban sprawl has an effect on natural areas even when it does not cause their direct destruction. Animals such as raccoons and white-tailed deer that have always been a part of natural communities in the Midwest suddenly undergo population explosions and become problems in isolated preserves surrounded by developed land. It may take decades for the full effects of urban sprawl to reveal themselves. In an environment of concrete and chemically treated lawns, the preservation of natural areas is a major challenge.

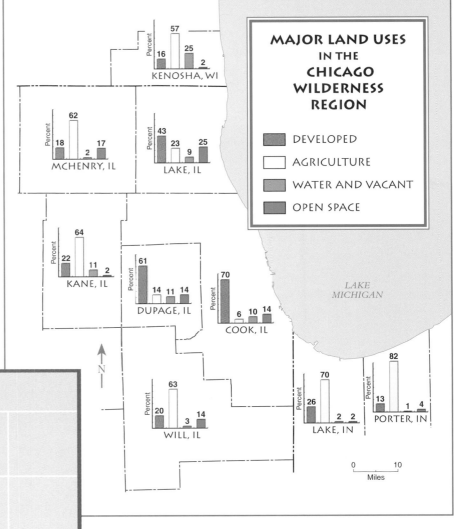

MAJOR LAND USES IN THE CHICAGO WILDERNESS REGION

- DEVELOPED
- AGRICULTURE
- WATER AND VACANT
- OPEN SPACE

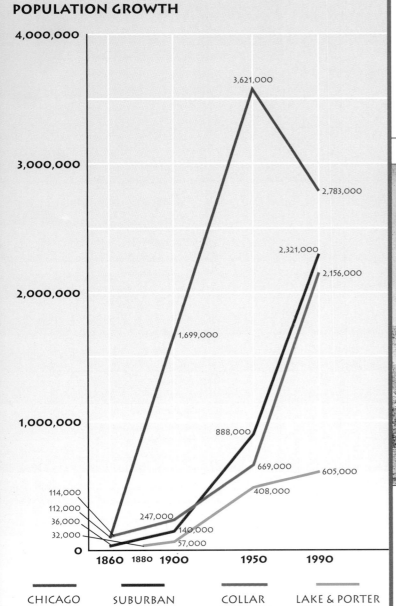

POPULATION GROWTH

4,000,000

3,621,000

3,000,000

2,783,000

2,321,000
2,156,000

2,000,000

1,699,000

1,000,000

888,000

669,000
605,000
408,000

114,000
112,000
36,000
32,000

247,000
140,000
57,000

0

1860   1880   1900   1950   1990

CHICAGO   SUBURBAN   COLLAR   LAKE & PORTER
                 COOK COUNTY   COUNTIES   COUNTIES, IN

This drawing from an atlas published in 1870 shows a section of the DesPlaines River near Plainfield in Will County. The varied landscape of prairies and groves became a landscape of plowed fields and woodlots as settlement advanced.

PEOPLE ON THE LAND
The Creation of the Forest Preserves

A pathway leads invitingly into Will County's Messenger Woods. Wildlife from coyotes to white-tailed deer are residents of local preserves.

Members of a committee that first proposed the idea of a system of natural preserves in Cook County. Dwight Perkins (center right), an architect, led the effort to make this idea a reality.

The early years of the twentieth century were a time when Americans began to look at the effects of our growing civilization on the natural environment. The belief of earlier times that the resources of North America were limitless no longer seemed to fit. The frontier was gone. The buffalo nearly killed off. The vast flocks of passenger pigeons that once darkened the skies of eastern North America were extinct. We had lost much and clearly we stood to lose much more if we did not change the way we thought about the land.

It was a time when the U.S. Forest Service and the National Park Service were created, a time when the first National Wildlife Refuges were set aside. There was even a proposal put forward to create a national park at the Indiana Dunes.

In Chicago, an organization called the Municipal Science Club headed by architects Jens Jensen and Dwight H. Perkins proposed that the most beautiful natural areas remaining in Cook County be set aside "for the benefit of the public."

It took 15 years of work to turn that idea into reality, but in 1915, Forest Preserve Districts were created in Cook and DuPage Counties. Land purchases began immediately with a 79-acre tract in DuPage County and 500 acres at Deer Grove near Palatine in Cook County.

The essential idea of the forest preserves was to preserve the native flora and fauna of the region for the "education, pleasure, and recreation of the public." The outcome has been to offer generations of city dwellers a

chance to experience nature within a few minutes travel of their homes while simultaneously offering protection to a broad range of natural communities that have been wiped out through most of their former range.

In the following years, the state of Indiana created a park at the Dunes, while Illinois developed parks at Illinois Beach and Chain O'Lakes and later a large Conservation Area where the Kankakee and Des Plaines Rivers join to form the Illinois and another park at Goose Lake in Grundy County.

In the years after World War II, as people began moving in ever larger numbers into the counties around Cook County, Lake, Kane, and Will Counties in Illinois and Lake County, Indiana created their own forest preserve districts. In 1971, McHenry County founded a Conservation District to hold and manage natural lands.

In 1966, 50 years after it was first proposed, the Indiana Dunes National Lakeshore became a reality. Most recently, the old Joliet Arsenal was converted into the Midewin National Tallgrass prairie, adding 15,000 acres of public natural land to the region.

We are lucky that our history has given us 200,000 acres of preserved natural land not "near to," but right in the middle of one of the largest metropolitan areas in the country. Few metropolises can equal this total.

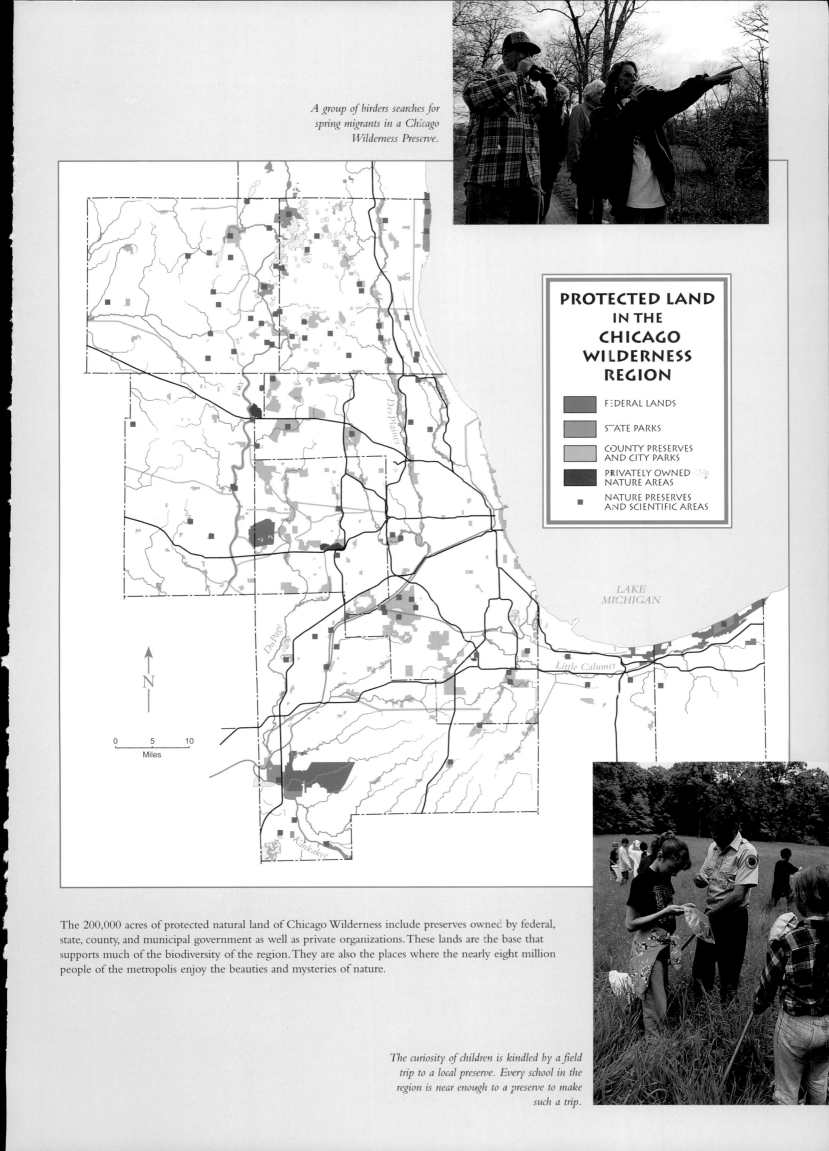

A group of birders searches for spring migrants in a Chicago Wilderness Preserve.

PROTECTED LAND IN THE CHICAGO WILDERNESS REGION

FEDERAL LANDS

STATE PARKS

COUNTY PRESERVES AND CITY PARKS

PRIVATELY OWNED NATURE AREAS

NATURE PRESERVES AND SCIENTIFIC AREAS

LAKE MICHIGAN

N

0 5 10
Miles

The 200,000 acres of protected natural land of Chicago Wilderness include preserves owned by federal, state, county, and municipal government as well as private organizations. These lands are the base that supports much of the biodiversity of the region. They are also the places where the nearly eight million people of the metropolis enjoy the beauties and mysteries of nature.

The curiosity of children is kindled by a field trip to a local preserve. Every school in the region is near enough to a preserve to make such a trip.

PEOPLE ON THE LAND
Restoration and Management

May Theilgard Watts

In books and classes at the Morton Arboretum, she taught that the landscape is intelligible and that people can enrich their lives by learning to read it.

Human beings have been helping to shape the wonderfully diverse landscape of the Chicago region for thousands of years. The Native American setting fire to the golden grasses of the prairie autumn was giving an assist to the natural processes that sustained fire-dependent communities. Bending natural processes to the needs of humans, the native people could take what they needed from the environment without harming the ecosystems that supported them.

The flood of settlers that swept across the Midwest in the past 175 years arrived with no knowledge of the workings of the native natural communities. They imposed demands upon the land that the land could not sustain. Some ecosystems were lost on land that became farms and towns; others were lost simply because the new people did not know how to protect them.

The process called ecological restoration uses the knowledge gained over the past 200 years to restore and maintain the biodiversity of this region. As it restores the natural communities, it also restores the old human tie to the land, helping us function as benefactors instead of destroyers.

We can date the beginning of ecological restoration in the Midwest to a time about 60 years ago when scientists at the University of Wisconsin began planting tallgrass prairie species at the University's Arboretum in Madison. That restored ecosystem continues to be improved to this day.

It is not surprising that restoration began with an effort to restore a tallgrass prairie. The prairie, which once covered thousands of square miles in the Midwest, was approaching extinction in the thirties. It obviously needed help.

Those first prairie restorationists were also the first managers to apply fire as a tool of prairie protection. At the time, this was a daring step that was roundly condemned by many who considered fires to be totally destructive.

The first prairie restoration in the Chicago area was begun by Ray Schulenberg at the Morton Arboretum in 1962. Schulenberg used horticultural techniques, hand-planting prairie species and weeding around them to remove competition. He began with just half an acre,

**RESTORATION SITES
IN THE
CHICAGO
WILDERNESS
REGION**

Fox

DesPlaines

*LAKE
MICHIGAN*

Little Calumet

Kankakee

N

0   10
Miles

A close collaboration among scientists, land managers, and citizen volunteers is bringing the benefits of restoration to natural areas throughout the region.

The federally endangered lakeside daisy (Actinea herbacea), once extirpated in the region, has been reestablished on a dolomite prairie in Will County where it is currently doing well.

John Rogner of the US Fish & Wildlife Service hand pollinates flowers of the federally threatened prairie white-fringed orchid.

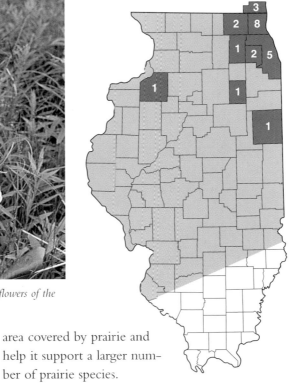

Illinois Populations of the Prairie White-fringed Orchid

*This flower (*Habenaria leucophaea*) once ranged over most of Illinois. The numbers show numbers of surviving populations in each county. The existence of these populations has made the Chicago region the center of recovery efforts for the species.*

although the Schulenberg Prairie has now expanded to 80 acres with an additional 20 acres of oak savanna.

For Dr. Robert F. Betz of Northeastern Illinois University, a man with an intense interest in reviving the prairie, the Schulenberg Prairie represented a major step forward. It showed that diversity could be established in a prairie restoration and provided significant information on how to go about the task. But Betz thought Schulenberg's restoration was too small to, in his words "hold all the species." Holding all the species was a task that demanded space, and a restoration project on the necessary scale could not be done by hand.

In 1972, Betz got permission to conduct prairie restoration at the Fermi National Accelerator Lab in Batavia, IL. Working with Lab staff and volunteers, he planted his first seeds in 1975. Initially, the project concentrated on the 600 acres that lay inside the accelerator's enormous ring. Gathering seeds with a combine and planting them with a machine that had been used to spread salt on highways has allowed the project to be expanded to 1,000 acres. The older parts now support populations of more than 80 species of prairie plants.

In the late seventies, restoration techniques began to be applied to surviving prairies. These prairies were small remnants where some prairie species could be found growing along with various weeds, shrubs, and small trees. Seeds of prairie species gathered from other sites could be sowed into these remnants. This enrichment, combined with the removal of the woody brush and periodic prescribed burns, could expand the area covered by prairie and help it support a larger number of prairie species.

RESTORING THE WOODLANDS

While prairies were the center of attention for restoration in its early decades, the eighties saw a major expansion of concern. The condition of those quintessentially Midwestern communities—the oak woodlands and savannas—was obviously worsening. Scarcely any savannas had survived, and those that did remain had been so heavily affected by the changes that settlement brought that an intense scientific debate broke out over the fundamental question of what they had been like. Were they simply ecotones—transition zones between forests and prairies? Or were they distinctive communities? Were they places where oaks grew over a ground layer of prairie plants?

Volunteers in training to monitor butterfly populations check a site for lepidopterans. The nationally recognized program is operating on sites throughout the region.

Populations of the rare Baltimore checkerspot soar at burned areas of Nelson Lake Marsh in Kane County.

Floyd Swink

Long-time chief taxonomist at the Morton Arboretum, he taught generations of students to recognize and appreciate the native landscape. His book, Plants of the Chicago Region, *is the ultimate authority on the botany of Chicago Wilderness.*

Or was there a savanna plant community different from either prairies or forests?

The oak woodlands had survived the initial shock of the post settlement changes, but study after study found that the oaks in these communities were not reproducing. Sugar maples were becoming dominant trees, but the species lost to the heavy shade of the maples were not being replaced by typical maple forest species. Instead of ecological succession replacing an oak forest with a maple forest, ecological degeneration was replacing oak forests with a depauperate landscape of a few trees, a few weeds, and a lot of bare earth. Plainly conservationists needed to think beyond the edges of the prairie.

VOLUNTEERS LEND A HAND

The slow hand-work of the first restoration projects was quite unlike the industrial style of the Fermi Lab project, but the effects of this

protecting the earth, led to the formation of other volunteer groups. Changes in environmental laws were also focusing attention on restoration of all sorts of natural communities—wetlands as well as forests, savannas, and prairies.

With the organizational backing of The Nature Conservancy, thousands of volunteers throughout Illinois were recruited for the Volunteer Stewardship Network. The volunteers work in collaboration with land-owning agencies—chiefly the county forest preserve and conservation districts—on a wide range of restoration projects. The volunteers supplement the work of agency staff members, providing tens of thousands of hours of free labor. Some of this labor is the sheer hard work of cutting and removing invasive species like common buckthorn. Some requires a sophisticated scientific knowledge and the experience that only long hours in the field can provide.

A burn site at Indiana Dunes National Lakeshore looked blackened and charred right after the fire, but new growth, stimulated by the blaze, quickly clothes it in bright new greenery.

hand labor began to accumulate, thanks to a growing group of volunteers who donated their time to restoration projects. Restoration could be done by hand if you could get enough hands involved.

The first volunteer ecological restoration work was done in the preserves along the North Branch of the Chicago River in Cook County beginning in 1977. The volunteers called themselves the North Branch Prairie Project. As volunteers for the Forest Preserve District of Cook County, they recruited and organized interested people to carry on the work.

The results they got, and the enthusiasm they inspired in people whose love of nature made them eager to make a direct contribution to

Volunteers study ecology and land management, and, increasingly, ecologists and land managers recognize volunteers as sources of practical information on ecology.

The volunteers also offer the land managers thousands of extra pairs of eyes. They are often the first people to notice the presence of a rare species in a preserve. They also notice problems like illegal dumping or the place where off-road-vehicles are entering a preserve. Working on restoration projects has made people more effective conservationists. They are informed supporters of our preserve systems and pioneers in changing the way people in a modern industrial society relate to nature. They are helping put people back in the natural landscape in a constructive way.

Setting a back fire to create a fire break during a prescribed burn.

INCREASED BIODIVERSITY

	1985-86	1986-87	1988	1989	1991
NUMBER OF SPECIES	11.6	13.5	19.5	17.9	18.1
NUMBER OF NATIVE SPECIES	9.0	10.8	16.2	15.2	16.6
FQA*	3.8	6.4	10.2	11.4	13.5

FQA: Floristic Quality Assessment from Swink and Wilhelm.

These are average numbers for 15 plots, each one square meter, in Vestal Grove, an oak savanna/woodland at Somme Woods Forest Preserve in northern Cook County. Restoration began in 1984. The plots were sampled twice, spring and fall. Fall, 1985 and Spring, 1986 data were combined, as were Fall 1986 and Spring, 1987. Thereafter, spring and fall samplings were done in the same year.

THE HOW OF RESTORATION

The lands in the preserves of the Chicago Wilderness range from beautiful natural areas filled with rare native species to former corn fields covered with weeds. Each piece of land has a unique history: How long ago was this woods logged? Was it grazed? Have drainage projects lowered the water table and killed off wetland vegetation?

The process of developing a management plan begins with a survey of what is there now and historical research into what was there in the past. The plan may call for the protection or expansion of natural communities already present, or, in the case of the cornfields, natural quality can be built from scratch. Each site is unique, so each plan is unique, but there are some common problems that need to be addressed on many sites. These include:

• Changes in hydrology. If a site was drained by field tile, removing the tile can restore the old water regime and make possible the reestablishment of the native natural community.

• Invasion by aggressive exotic plants. Only a few of the more than 500 species of plants introduced into the Chicago region in the past 200 years create problems, but those few make a lot of trouble. Whether it is common buckthorn (*Rhamnus cathartica*) in a woodland or purple loosestrife (*Lythrum salicaria*) in a marsh, the exotics can drive out both native plants and native wildlife. Restoration may involve physical removal of exotics and/or the use of herbicides to kill them.

• Thinning of native trees to allow more light to reach the ground. This promotes the growth of native plants of savannas and woodlands—including young oaks. The technique may also be used to protect the plants of fens and sedge meadows.

• Planting the seeds of native species typical of the natural community or to establish a community on old fields or other waste land.

• Returning fire to the ecosystem.

The ultimate aims are to return the species typical of the community to the land and to recreate the ecological forces that sustained the community in the past. Thus far, restoration has successfully expanded the ranges of rare species and rare ecosystems in the Chicago region. The work here has been taken as a model by conservationists around the globe. It represents our best hope for preserving the biodiversity of Chicago Wilderness.

Restoration Goals

Restore
natural processes.

Restock
lost species of
plants and animals.

Maintain
natural ecosystems in
good health.

Restoration heals the land and enriches the spirits of those who do it.

CHICAGO WILDERNESS

Chicago Wilderness is supported by the Chicago Region Biodiversity Council, an unprecendented partnership of public and private organizations that have joined forces to protect, restore and manage these natural lands and the plants and animals that inhabit them.

Chicago Wilderness seems to be an oxymoron, but this region harbors some of the best remnants of our Midwest "wilderness"— our native plant and animal communities—remaining on earth. It is only through active protection, management and restoration that the prairies, woodlands and wetlands comprising Chicago Wilderness will survive.

The member organizations of the Chicago Region Biodiversity Council, and the thousands of volunteers who work with them, are pooling their resources and expertise to most effectively protect, manage and restore the natural heritage of the central Midwest.

ORGANIZATIONS OF THE CHICAGO REGION BIODIVERSITY COUNCIL

For information about Chicago Wilderness, visit our web site at www.chiwild.org.

Individuals can participate in Chicago Wilderness activities throughout the region. To learn about these opportunities, call the Chicagoland Environmental Network (708)485-0263 ext. 396.

Brookfield Zoo
3300 Golf Rd.
Brookfield, IL 60513-0719
(708)485-0263

Canal Corridor Association
220 S. State St., Suite 1880
Chicago, IL 60604
(312)427-3688

Chicago Academy of Sciences
2060 N. Clark St.
Chicago, IL 60614
(773)549-0606

★Chicago Botanic Garden
Lake Cook Road
P.O. Box 400
Glencoe, IL 60022-0400
(847)835-5440

★Chicago Park District
425 E. McFetridge Dr.
Chicago, IL 60605
(312)747-2200

★City of Chicago, Department of Environment
30 N. LaSalle St. #2500
Chicago, IL 60602-2505
(312)744-7606

The Field Museum
Roosevelt Rd at Lake Shore Drive
Chicago, IL 60605-2496
(312)922-9410

★Forest Preserve District of Cook County
536 N. Harlem Ave.
River Forest, IL 60305
(708)366-9420

★Forest Preserve District of DuPage County
185 Spring Ave.
P.O. Box 2339
Glen Ellyn, IL 60138
(630)790-4900

★Forest Preserve District of Will County
22606 Cherry Hill Rd.
Joliet, IL 60433
(815)727-8700

Friends of the Chicago River
407 S. Dearborn St. #1580
Chicago, IL 60605
(312)939-0490

★Illinois Department of Natural Resources
524 S. Second Street
Springfield, IL 62701
(217)782-6302

Illinois Natural History Survey
607 E. Peabody Dr.
Champaign, IL 61820
(217)333-5986

★Illinois Nature Preserves Commission
524 S. Second St.
Springfield, IL 62701
(217)785-8686

★Kane County Forest Preserve District
719 S. Batavia Ave.
Geneva, IL 60134
(630)232-5980

★Lake County Forest Preserves
2000 N. Milwaukee Ave.
Libertyville, IL 60048-1199
(847)367-3676

Lake Michigan Federation
59 E. Van Buren St. #2215
Chicago, IL 60605
(312)939-0838

Lincoln Park Zoo
2200 N. Cannon Dr.
Chicago, IL 60614
(312)742-2353

★McHenry County Conservation District
6512 Harts Rd.
Ringwood, IL 60072
(815)678-4431

★Metropolitan Water Reclamation District of Greater Chicago
100 E. Erie St.
Chicago, IL 60611
(312)751-6634

★Morton Arboretum
Route 53
Lisle, IL 60532
(630)968-0074

★The Nature Conservancy
8 S. Michigan Ave. #900
Chicago, IL 60603
(312)346-8166

Northeastern Illinois Planning Commission
222 S. Riverside Plaza #1800
Chicago, IL 60606
(312)454-0400

Openlands Project
220 S. State St. #1880
Chicago, IL 60604-2103
(312)427-4256

John G. Shedd Aquarium
1200 S. Lake Shore Dr.
Chicago, IL 60605
(312)939-2438

Sierra Club, Illinois Chapter
1 N. LaSalle St. #4242
Chicago, IL 60602
(312)251-1680

Urban Resources Partnership
c/o US Department of Housing and Urban Development
77 W. Jackson Blvd.
Chicago, IL 60604
(312)353-2473

US Army Corps of Engineers, Chicago District
111 N. Canal St. #600
Chicago, IL 60606
(312)353-6400

US Environmental Protection Agency Region 5
77 W. Jackson Blvd.
Chicago, IL 60604-3590
(312)886-7935

US EPA Great Lakes National Program Office
77 W. Jackson Blvd.
Chicago, IL 60604-3590
(312)886-7935

US Fish & Wildlife Service
1000 Hart Rd. #180
Barrington, IL 60010
(847)381-2253

★USDA Forest Service
845 Chicago Ave. #225
Evanston, IL 60202-2357
(847)866-9311

USDA Natural Resources Conservation Service
603 E. Diehl Rd., #131
Naperville, IL 60563-1476
(630)505-7808

★USDI National Park Service
1709 Jackson St.
Omaha, NE 68102
(402)221-3471

★Organizations marked with an asterisk own and/or manage natural lands. Contact them for information on visiting these lands to see the natural wonders of Chicago Wilderness.

SUGGESTIONS FOR FURTHER READING

Bohlen, H David, *The Birds of Illinois*, Indiana University Press, Bloomington, 1989.

Brock, Kenneth J., *Birds of the Indiana Dunes*, Indiana University Press, Bloomington, Ind., 1986.

Cronon, William, *Nature's Metropolis*, W.W. Norton & Co., New York, 1991

Curtis, John T., *Vegetation of Wisconsin*, U. of Wisconsin Press, Madison, 1959.

Daniel, Glenda L., *Dune Country*, 2nd Ed., illus. by Carol Lerner, Swallow Press, Athens, OH, 1984.

Eckert, Allan W., *Gateway to Empire*, Bantam Books, New York City, 1983.

Eggers, Steve D. and Donald M. Reed, *Wetland Plants and Plant Communities of Minnesota and Wisconsin*, US Army Corps of Engineers, St. Paul District, St. Paul, MN, 1987.

Engel, J. Ronald, *Sacred Sands*, Wesleyan University Press, Middletown, CN, 1983.

A Field Guide to the Wetlands of Illinois, Illinois Dept. of Natural Resources, 1988.

The Great Lakes, An Environmental Atlas and Resource Book, 3rd Ed., USEPA Great Lakes National Program Office and Government of Canada, Chicago, 1995.

Hofmeister, Donald F. *Mammals of Illinois*, U. of Illinois Press, Urbana and Chicago, 1989.

Ladd, Doug, *Tallgrass Prairie Wildflowers*, photos by Frank Oberle, Falcon Press Publishing, Helena, Mont., 1995.

Lampa, Wayne, *The Phoenix Land*, Forest Preserve District of DuPage County, N.D.

Leopold, Aldo, *Sand County Almanac*, Oxford University Press, New York City, 1949.

Madson, John, *Where the Sky Began*, Houghton Mifflin Co., Boston, MA, 1982.

Mills, Stephanie, *In Service of the Wild*, Beacon Press, Boston, 1995.

Mlodinow, Steven, *Chicago Area Birds*, Chicago Review Press, Chicago, 1984. Copies available from Chicago Audubon Society.

Packard, Stephen and Cornelia F. Mutel, eds., *The Tallgrass Restoration Handbook*, Island Press, Washington, D.C., 1997.

Peattie, Donald Culross, *Flora of the Indiana Dunes*, Field Museum of Natural History, Chicago, 1930.

Pepoon, H.S., *An Annotated Flora of the Chicago Area*, Chicago Academy of Sciences, Chicago, 1927.

Pielou, E. C., *After the Ice Age*, University of Chicago Press, Chicago, 1991.

Randall, John and James Marinelli, eds., *Invasive Plants, The Weeds of the Global Garden*, Brooklyn Botanic Garden, Brooklyn, NY, 1996.

Smith, Philip W., *The Amphibians and Reptiles of Illinois*, Illinois Natural History Survey, Urbana, 1961.

Stevens, William K., *Miracle Under the Oaks*, Pocket Books, New York City, 1995.

Straus, Terry, ec., *Indians of the Chicago Area*, NAES College, Chicago, 1990.

Swink, Floyd and Gerould Wilhelm, *Plants of the Chicago Region*, 4th ed., Indiana Academy of Science, Indianapolis, IN, 1994.

Tanner, Helen, *Atlas of Great Lakes Indian History*, U. of Oklahoma Press, Norman, OK, 1987.

Watts, May T, *Reading the Landscape*, Macmillan Publishing Co., New York City, 1975.

Willman, H.B., *Summary of the Geology of the Chicago Area*, IL State Geological Survey, Urbana, IL, 1971.

Wilson, E.O., *The Diversity of Life*, Norton, New York City, 1992.

Young, Dick, *Kane County Wild Plants and Natural Areas*, 2nd ec., Kane County Forest Preserve District, Geneva, IL, 1994.

Good Field Guides are available to practically everything in nature. In general, guides to the eastern U.S. will cover the Chicago region.

ACKNOWLEDGEMENTS

Many people contributed to this Atlas by providing information, advice, and review of manuscripts. The list includes: James Steffen and Susanne Masi of the Chicago Botanic Garden; Gerould Wilhelm of the Conservation Design Forum; Greg Mueller, Jack Murphy, and Daniel Summers of the Field Museum; Ralph Thornton, Steven Thomas, and John Elliott of the Forest Preserve District of Cook County; Wayne Lampa and JoEllen Siddens of the Forest Preserve District of Du Page County; Marcella DeMauro of the Forest Preserve District of Will County; Chris Parsons of the Friends of the Chicago River; Brian Anderson, Vernon Kleen, Steven Pescetelli of the Illinois Department of Natural Resources; James Herkert of the Illinois Endangered Species Board; Ardith Hansel and Michael Chrzastowski of the Illinois State Geological Survey; Scott Robinson and Christopher Phillips of the Illinois Natural History Survey; Steven Byers of the Illinois Nature Preserves Commission; John Bacone of the Indiana Nature Preserves Commission; Jon Duerr of the Kane County Forest Preserve District; Andy Kimmel, James Anderson, and Ken Klick of the Lake County Forest Preserves; Steven Christie of Lake Forest Open Lands; Wayne Schennum, Ed Collins, and Susan Ladendorf of the McHenry County Conservation District; Marlin Bowles, Christopher Dunn, and Jenny McBride of the Morton Arboretum; Katie Green, Stephen Packard, Laurel Ross, and Sandi Stein of The Nature Conservancy; Richard Mariner of the Northeastern Illinois Planning Commission; Lauren Rhein of the Northwestern Indiana Regional Planning Commission; Glenda Daniel of the Openlands Project; Donald M. Reed of the Southeastern Wisconsin Regional Planning Commission; Kenneth Mierzwa of TAMS Consultants; Dr. Dennis Nyberg, UIC; Jean Sellar of the US Army Corps of Engineers, Chicago District; Kent Fuller of US EPA Great Lakes National Program Office; John Rogner and Amelia Orton-Palmer of the US Fish & Wildlife Service; Mark Bramstedt of the USDA Natural Resources Conservation Service; John and Jane Balaban of the Volunteer Stewardship Network; Kenneth Brock; Joseph Milosevich; Ron Panzer.

CREDITS

Map Credits

The map of surficial deposits on Page 7 was created by the **USDA Natural Resources Conservation Service**. All other maps were drawn by **Richard Vaupel** and **Leonard Walther** of the Cartography Lab at **Northern Illinois University**, DeKalb, IL. Illinois areas were placed on a base map prepared by **NIPC** and **Openlands Project**.

Map Sources

Page 4, E&T Species of Illinois, **Illinois Endangered Species Board**; Rare and Endangered Communities, created by **TAMS Consultants**; Page 10, **Ill. Geological Survey**; Page 11, **IDNR** and **TAMS Consultants**; Pages 12-13, **Lake County Forest Preserves**, **Robbin C. Moran**, **Philip J. Hansen**, **FPD of Will County**, **SEWRPC**, INHS map by **R.C. Anderson**, report to INDU by **John Bacone** and **Gerould Wilhelm**; Page 13, **TNC**; Page 16, **FPDs of Cook, DuPage, Will, Cook, Kane Counties, Lake County FP, McHenry CCD, Ill. Nat. Pres. Comm., Ind. Nat. Pres. Comm.**; Page 20, **Chicago Audubon Soc.** nesting bird census, 1995; Page 28, **Marlin Bowles, Jenny McBride**; Page 35, **INHS**; Page 40, **USFWS**; Page 41, **IDNR, Kenneth J. Brock**; Pages 43 and 44, **INHS**; Page 47, **IDNR**; Page 50, **Atlas of Great Lakes Indians**; Page 53, **NIPC, NW Ind. RPC, SEWRPC**; Page 55, **Openlands Project, NIPC, Lake County FP, FPDs of Will, DuPage, Kane, and Cook Counties, McHenry CCD, INDU, SEWRPC, Lake County (IN) Parks and Recreation Board**; Page 56, **VSN**; Page 57, **USFWS**.

Photo and art credits

Front and back cover; pps. 14-15, top; p. 18, prairie violet, common cinquefoil, wild strawberry, hoary puccoon, false toadflax; p.19, wild onion, early goldenrod, Indian grass, heath aster; p. 31, fox squirrel; p. 54, woods: **Bill Glass**. Cover butterfly/p. 60; Title page butterfly; p. 22, all images: **Ron Panzer**. Contents page and p. 30, scarlet tanager; p.18, spiderwort; p.20, upland sandpiper, dickcissel; p. 21, grasshopper sparrow; p. 30, hairy woodpecker, northern oriole, ovenbird, red-headed woodpecker; p. 31, red-tailed hawk; p. 40/p. 60, moorhen; p. 41, sora rail: **Rob Curtis**. Pages 4-5, p. 29, trillium in forest; p. 38, ladyslippers; p.59, burn: **Steve Packard**. Pages 8, 9, 25, 30, 34, 36, 37, 38, 45, 48, 53, 59, graphics and artwork: **Corasue Nicholas**. Page 9, esker: **Jerry Sullivan**. Page 14, Turk's cap lily: **The Prairie Arts/L. Gits & L. Godson**. Page 15, drawing: **Nancy Halliday**. Page 16, Dr. Betz; p. 54, fawn: **The Nature Conservancy**. Pages16-17, fire; p.33, massasauga; Page 55, photos: **Lake County FP**. Page 17, drawing: **Carol Lerner**. Page 17, new growth; p. 40, dragonfly: **Dave and Lorene Jagodzinski**. Page 18, prairie phlox, **David Sollenberger**. Page 18, prairie cinquefoil, LeConte's violet, prairie alum root; p. 18 and Contents page, starry false solomon's seal; p. 19, Kalm's brome, sky blue aster: **John and Jane Balaban**. Page 18, common blue-eyed grass, heart-leaved meadow parsnip; p. 19, prairie gray sedge, copper-shouldered oval sedge: **Ken Dritz**. Page 18, wild quinine, p. 19, prairie dock, rough blazing star, little bluestem, New England aster: **Thomas Antonio**. Page 18, rattlesnake master; p. 19 marsh blazing star: **Kent Fuller**. Page 19, yellow coneflower: **K. Taylor**. Page 19, bearded wheatgrass; p. 54, committee: **FPD of Cook County**. Page 21, sandhill crane: **International Crane Foundation**. Page 23, bison; p.27/p. 61, maple leaves; p.31, gray squirrel; p. 32, all images; p. 33, gray tree frog and chorus frog; p. 34/p. 63, Cowles' Bog; p. 36, button bush; p. 39, Volo Bog, sundew; p. 42/p. 63, river otter; p. 43, Blanding's turtle; p. 46, river; p.48, Fowler's toad; p. 54, coyote: **James P. Rowan**. Page 23, smooth green snake: **Kenneth S. Mierzwa**. Page 24, bur oak; p.36, smartweeds: **Wayne Lampa**. Page 24/p.62, marsh marigolds; p. 49, dunes; p. 58, before and after photos: **Bob Daum**. Pages 26-27, drawings, bur oak leaves: **Lana Gits**. Page 27, photo: **Ralph Thornton**. Page 28, photo: **Jim Anderson**. Page 29, earth star; p. 42, beaver lodge, tree; p. 43, baby snappers; p. 50, women building lodge: **Ind. Dunes Nat. Lkshre.** Page 29, coral fungus: **Jack Murphy**. Page 30, bluebird: **Kim Harris/TNC**. Page 37, 45, photos; p.47, stream; p. 57, pollination: **USFWS**. Page 38, both photos; p. 39, grass pink: **Steve Byers**. Page 41, egrets: **Joe B. Milosevich**. Page 44, fish; p. 47, fish, channelized stream: **Illinois DNR**. Page 48, H. C. Cowles: **UC/Regensteiner Library**. Page 49, zebra mussels: **US EPA**. Page 51, Du Sable site: **Friends of the River**. Page 52, both images: **Deere & Company**. Page 53, 1873 view of the Des Plaines: **Openlands Project**. Page 55, lakeside daisies: **Marcy DeMauro**. Page 56, May Watts: **The Illinois Prairie Path**. Page 57, butterfly monitors: **Doug Taron**. Page 58, Floyd Swink: **The Morton Arboretum**. Page 58, kids in pink caps: **Christopher Kean**.

INDEX

SPECIES INDEX

CHICAGO WILDERNESS

A Regional Nature Reserve

The enclosed book *Chicago Wilderness: An Atlas of Biodiversity* contains information on the surprisingly rich biological region stretching from Kenosha, Wisconsin through the Indiana Dunes. It has been produced on behalf of the Chicago Region Biodiversity Council, a cooperative group of governmental and not-for-profit organizations that share an interest in protecting the biological treasures of the greater Chicago region.

We hope you will enjoy learning about the habitats and natural communities of the region as an informed participant in the large and small decisions to protect these spectacular places for future generations. Chicago Wilderness is all around us, but so are the threats to the health of these natural communities. By understanding, protecting and restoring ecological health, we enrich biodiversity and wildlife habitat, and enrich our own quality of life as well.

It is not too late to protect these "Natural Wonders" or to enjoy them for yourself. To learn more about Chicago Wilderness and how you can get involved, call the Chicagoland Environmental Network at (708)485-0263 ext. 396, or visit our Web Site at *www.chiwild.org*.

Sincerely,

Phillip D. Peters

Phillip D. Peters
Executive Director, Northeastern Illinois Planning Commission
Chair, Chicago Region Biodiversity Council